Evelyn B. Rosenthal, who holds degrees from Vassar and Radcliffe colleges, has taught mathematics for nearly thirty years at the Fieldston School in New York City. Miss Rosenthal, who has also taught Latin, is the author of articles published in *The Mathematics Teacher*, a journal of the National Council of Teachers of Mathematics, and is the co-author of a text in use in the mathematics program at the Fieldston School, *Geometry, a Coordinated Approach to Mathematics*. She makes her home in New York.

Understanding the New Mathematics

Evelyn B. Rosenthal

A Fawcett Crest Book

FAWCETT PUBLICATIONS, INC., GREENWICH, CONN.
MEMBER OF AMERICAN BOOK PUBLISHERS COUNCIL, INC.

The Author and Publisher acknowledge permission to reprint the following cartoons:

Page 13 Drawing by Jerry Marcus; reprinted by permission of the artist.

Page 10 Copyright 1951, reprinted by permission of the Bell-McClure Syndicate.

Page 24 Copyright 1954 by NEA Service, Inc. Reprinted by permission of Newspaper Enterprises Association, Inc.

Page 42 Drawing by Langley © 1963 by *The Christian Science Monitor.*

Page 58 Drawing by Paul Kaplan; © 1963 *The New York Standard.*

Page 72 Drawing by Hoff; © 1958 The New Yorker Magazine, Inc.

Page 74 Drawing by Stan Fine in the *Saturday Evening Post,* reprinted by permission of the artist.

Page 197 Drawing by Muriel Jacobs in the *Saturday Evening Post,* reprinted by permission of the artist.

Page 200 Drawing by Steinberg; © The New Yorker Magazine, Inc.

Page 231 Drawing by Richter; Copyright 1946 The New Yorker Magazine, Inc.

First Fawcett Crest printing, February 1965
Second Fawcett Crest printing, May 1965
Third Fawcett Crest printing, June 1965
Fourth Fawcett Crest printing, January 1966

Published by Fawcett World Library,
67 West 44th Street, New York, N. Y. 10036.

PRINTED IN THE UNITED STATES OF AMERICA

Contents

SECTION I

THE NEW MATH: AN INTRODUCTION   9

CHAPTER 1. — HOW TO READ THIS BOOK.   12

CHAPTER 2. — WHAT IT'S ALL ABOUT AND WHY.   13

Until recently, all the mathematics taught in school was known before the time of Newton. Although this older mathematics is still taught and is still useful, some newer developments are also important. Expanding technology is demanding more and better mathematicians. Many organizations and individuals have suggested ways of improving the mathematics curriculum. We stress the understanding of concepts and, where possible, the discovery of relationships rather than rote learning.

CHAPTER 3. — IN THE BEGINNING.   20

New trends in elementary-school mathematics are more in method than in content. However, topics that used to be reserved for high-school courses are started in a simple and intuitive way in some elementary-school programs.

SEEING NUMBER RELATIONSHIPS.   21

PATTERNS IN PICTURES.   25

IS IT ALGEBRA OR ARITHMETIC?   31

GEOMETRY, TOO.   33

SECTION II

ARITHMETIC AND ALGEBRA   35

CHAPTER 4. — THE NATURE OF NUMBERS AND NUMERALS.   38

The value of a numeral depends not only on its digits but also on the positions they occupy and on the base of the system. Normally we use the decimal system, based on counting by tens and powers of ten. It helps us understand the workings of this system if we study others. We can write numbers with bases other than ten and compute with them. The binary system, with a base of two, turns out to be useful in the design of computers.

THE BASE OF A NUMBER SYSTEM.   39

COMPUTING IN SYSTEMS WITH OTHER BASES.   47

v

THE BINARY SYSTEM.   57

CHAPTER 5. — SETS OF NUMBERS AND HOW THEY
BEHAVE.   61

Here we extend the idea of number from the positive whole
numbers, the simplest kind, to rational numbers, which include all the fractions. There are fundamental laws that govern mathematical operations.
Axioms are the foundation of algebra and arithmetic as well
as of geometry, and we use them to prove theorems in these
areas also. All the manipulations of arithmetic and algebra
follow logically from the axioms.

NATURAL NUMBERS AND COUNTING NUMBERS.   62

THE INTEGERS AND THE AXIOMS FOR ADDITION.   65

THE AXIOMS FOR MULTIPLICATION.   69

THE RATIONAL NUMBERS.   73

SOLVING EQUATIONS.   82

CHAPTER 6. — IS THURSDAY BEFORE OR AFTER MONDAY?   85

To show that there can be more than one arithmetic, we examine here some modular systems that have only a few numbers in them. They differ from ordinary arithmetic also in
that the concepts of "larger" and "smaller" that seem so
universal don't apply.

CLOCK-FACE ARITHMETIC.   85

ORDER.   92

CHAPTER 7. — FILLING IN THE HOLES.   97

Here we look at further extensions of the number system, and
go from the rational numbers to the real numbers and beyond.
Real numbers are what people usually mean when they speak
of "numbers."

BEYOND THE RATIONAL NUMBERS.   97

HOW MANY IS INFINITE?   104

SECTION III

ANALYTIC GEOMETRY.   111

CHAPTER 8. — FROM THE NUMBER LINE TO THE NUM-
BER PLANE.   113

A pair of numbers can be used to locate a point on a plane.
The two numbers of the pair may be connected by an equation or an inequality. The set of all points described by such
pairs is the graph of the relation. The concept of a "function"

is an important one, and we examine many sorts of functions. Solution sets of equations and of inequalities can be shown on the Cartesian plane. An interesting and useful application of sets of simultaneous inequalities is in *linear programming*.

RELATIONS AND FUNCTIONS. 114

GRAPHING SOLUTION SETS ON THE CARTESIAN PLANE. 134

LINEAR PROGRAMMING. 141

SECTION IV

SETS AND LOGIC. 148

CHAPTER 9. — MORE ABOUT SETS. 150

The idea of sets is an underlying one in mathematics. Several new symbols are needed to describe their relations. We can picture sets and operations with these symbols in many ways. There are axioms that govern the *union* and *intersection* of sets, which correspond roughly to addition and multiplication of numbers. Many problems can be visualized and solved by means of *set diagrams*.

NEW WORDS AND SYMBOLS. 150

THE RELATION BETWEEN TWO SETS. 155

VENN DIAGRAMS FOR THREE SETS. 163

THE ALGEBRA OF SETS. 171

CHAPTER 10. — MIND YOUR *p*'S AND *q*'S. 173

The study of logic, the nature of valid reasoning, is an important part of mathematics. Here we define the exact meaning of the little words used to make new statements out of old: *and, or, not,* and *if*. The axioms about combining statements turn out to be very similar—*mutatis mutandis*—to those about operations with sets. We can design electric circuits to illustrate them.

VENN DIAGRAMS IN LOGIC. 173

COMBINING STATEMENTS. 178

IMPLICATION. 182

WHAT DOES "ONLY IF" MEAN? 190

DIRECT AND INDIRECT PROOF. 193

BOOLEAN ALGEBRA. 194

SECTION V

GEOMETRIES: EUCLIDEAN, NON-EUCLIDEAN, AND OTHERS 199

CHAPTER 11. — EUCLID EXAMINED.   202

We stress the axiomatic method. One way to do this is by considering miniature geometries with a small number of elements. Another way is by examining the omissions in the traditional set of axioms. These axioms can be supplemented by many others to obtain a more rigorous system.

METHOD IN MATHEMATICS.   202

EUCLID IMPROVED.   207

CHAPTER 12. — EUCLID DISCARDED.   213

By changing one of Euclid's axioms, we can arrive at other consistent geometries. Topology can be very abstruse, but its simpler aspects are easy and fascinating. It is sometimes called *rubber-sheet geometry*. For example, if you draw a geometric figure on an elastic page and then distort it in any way, some properties do not change.

NON-EUCLIDEAN GEOMETRIES.   213

TOPOLOGY: GEOMETRY WITHOUT SIZE OR SHAPE.   217

SECTION VI

WHAT'S IT WORTH?   229

CHAPTER 13. — IS THERE MORE?   229

There are several other topics that have been suggested for inclusion in high-school courses and that are being used in some schools. Among them are *n*-dimensional geometry, groups, vectors, and matrices. Some traditional subjects are now taught with a different emphasis.

OTHER NEW TOPICS.   229

OTHER CHANGES.   232

CHAPTER 14. — CONCLUSION.   234

Mathematicians and mathematic teachers are not entirely in agreement about the value of the new courses. Here is an attempt to evaluate the programs and to indicate the directions in which further progress may be made.

SOME NEW WORDS AND SYMBOLS.   237

SUGGESTIONS FOR FURTHER READING.   239

SECTION I

The New Math:

An Introduction

Parents and children may have different ideas about many things. It is expected that they will not see eye to eye about clothes, conduct, manners, and a large variety of other topics. However, most of us feel that there are certain eternal verities about which everyone must agree, and mathematics should be one of these. Therefore, it is rather disconcerting to find a "new" mathematics which is strikingly different from the old.

Of course, school mathematics has not changed completely. In some schools, there are no perceptible differences, while in others, many new topics and ideas are being introduced. Even in these schools, much of what is being taught now is essentially the same as that which has been taught for years. Since this book is about the *new* mathematics, we will be discussing the aspects that have changed. You should realize, however, that there are many that have not.

Naturally, no one would expect current mathematics textbooks to be exactly like those of twenty or thirty years ago. Problems must reflect some changes: airplanes replace automobiles, as, earlier, automobiles replaced horses, in time-rate-and-distance problems; the bookkeeper's earnings no longer turn out to be around $20 a week; and those hard workers, the brothers Al, Bob, and Charles, who turn up in work problems as A, B, and C, are now more likely to be mowing suburban lawns than to be digging farm cisterns. Such changes are minor and do not bother anyone. It's not the same sort of thing at all when the children start talking about the binary system, Boolean algebra, and Moebius strips.

This can happen with youngsters at any age from early in elementary school to the late high-school years. There is as yet no set age level at which different new concepts are first

"Dad wants to know where to get the steak at 18 cents a pound in today's problems?"

taught, since schools are introducing new mathematics with varying degrees of timidity or enthusiasm. Whether a particular topic is taught in elementary school, in junior high school, or in high school frequently depends only on the availability of teachers willing and able to use some of the new ideas and methods. As more teachers are trained in the new mathematics, it seems likely that more of it will be introduced.

Parents and others who hear of these new concepts are naturally curious. Recently, in a suburban high school, an evening course for parents was arranged to discuss the new mathematics curriculum. The planners expected fifteen or twenty people to come; over two hundred showed up at the first meeting.

Parents are frequently puzzled by their children and eager to understand them better. For some of their problems, this may not be easy, but, at least as far as mathematics is concerned, communication and understanding can be re-established. It's not too difficult to learn something about the new mathematics as it is being taught in schools today.

Chapter 1

How to Read This Book

The best way to learn mathematics is to do mathematics. For that reason, most of these chapters have problems in them; in a few places, it was not feasible to include any. Of course, you can read the book without doing any of the problems. However, if you tackle them, do as many or as few as you like.

It's a good idea for you to try at first to do them without looking at the answers. If you get stuck, though, don't be afraid to look ahead at the answers and explanations. Some problems and sections are more difficult and may be omitted without serious loss; these are marked with an asterisk(*).

No mathematics book can be skimmed. Such books use many symbols which make it possible to say a lot in a very small space. In this respect, mathematics resembles shorthand. Besides, since the words and ideas represented are themselves often unfamiliar, it is like a new language. It takes a while to learn either shorthand or a foreign language well enough to be able to use it easily. That is, without a lot of practice, you wouldn't expect to be able to read fluently a letter written in shorthand in another language. So don't be discouraged if some of these pages look hard at first. Take your time and don't try to rush things!

Some of the more important new words and symbols are collected and defined on page 237. Refer to this if you need to refresh your memory.

Children in school don't learn these concepts all at once. Most of them are presented in a simple way early in a child's school career, and he meets them again and again in his twelve years of elementary and high school. No one can sit down and learn them in a few days. Some of the material is rather easy, but most of it is not. It takes careful reasoning and considerable thought to comprehend some of the ideas. Mathematical understanding can't be rushed.

Chapter 2
What It's All About and Why

Until recently, all the mathematics taught in school was known before the time of Newton. Although this older mathematics is still taught and is still useful, some newer developments

"How much was eight times twelve in your day?"

are also important. Expanding technology is demanding more and better mathematicians. Many organizations and individuals have suggested ways of improving the mathematics curriculum. We stress the understanding of concepts and, where possible, the discovery of relationships rather than rote learning.

Some time ago, a boy in one of my classes complained to me, "The homework for today was too hard. My mother couldn't do it." For years I told this story at parents' meetings, and it always got an appreciative laugh, but I don't tell it any more. I can't; it has lost its point. Mother can rarely help Johnny with his mathematics now. It's not that Mother is any less intelligent or that Johnny is any brighter than before, but that in many schools mathematics is not what it used to be. Frequently neither Mother nor Dad can understand what Johnny is talking about. Moreover, if Johnny's friend goes to another school where the curriculum in mathematics hasn't changed in the last five or six years, they probably can't understand each other either.

Why not? Are the new mathematics courses replete with new and different subject matter, incomprehensible to the uninitiated? Hardly. They do contain much that has been developed recently, but they also have in them most of the older material familiar to Mother and Dad and Johnny's friend. It seems strange to them partly because it is organized and arranged differently and partly because it uses different and more precise language and symbolism.

If Mother and Dad have had the usual amount of high-school mathematics, they know (unless they've forgotten it) all that Johnny is learning in elementary school; but the terms and symbols he uses may have baffled them so that they fail to realize it. If they have studied enough mathematics to take them through advanced algebra, nothing Johnny learns in junior high school should surprise them; but they may not understand what he is doing in senior high school unless they have had advanced college or graduate courses in mathematics.

This sounds as if children are now being forced to study very difficult subject matter at an early age. The opposite is true. Much of the new material is intrinsically easier than the traditional school courses. Teachers and curricula planners have finally realized what children and professional mathematicians have known all along—that arithmetic is hard. Carl Friedrich Gauss (1777–1855), who pioneered in the theory of numbers, said, "Mathematics is the Queen of the Sciences and Arithmetic the Queen of Mathematics." A real understanding of arithmetic requires considerable mathematical maturity and imagination. Of course it takes little of either to learn arithmetic facts and processes by rote. Rote is what elementary-school children have been using for years. With little or no emphasis on the reasons behind the manipulations or on the structure of the system, only long and repeated drills can produce the desired proficiency. Meaningless drill and rote learning sometimes do teach mechanically accurate computation. They also frequently result in a permanent deep distaste for arithmetic and all mathematics. One aim of the new programs is to avoid this pitfall. Mathematics is essentially a logical structure full of beautiful patterns. Why not enjoy discovering them?

Another aim, of course, is to bring some current and recent developments in mathematics to the average student. A traditional high-school course contains nothing that was not known at the time of Isaac Newton; anything discovered or created after the middle of the seventeenth century is not included. A student who takes two years of traditional college mathematics goes a little further, but he learns no nineteenth- or twentieth-century mathematics.

Of course, much beautiful and useful mathematics was developed early. We don't want to throw away the old in order to embrace the new. Classica, traditional mathematics is still invaluable for engineers, pharmacists, surveyors, navigators, and scientists of all kinds; but it is insufficient for many of the needs of modern technology. Industry and business now have work for more mathematicians than our colleges and universities can produce, and much of that work requires modern mathematics. In particular, the spreading use of computers and the increasing need for statistical techniques have pointed up the need for a new and different mathematics.

Many mathematicians would consider the previous paragraph irrelevant. For them, applications and uses are for the engineer, and the only real mathematician is a pure mathematician. (A pure mathematician may be defined as one who is distressed if anyone dreams up a use for his work. Unfortunately for him, unexpected applications crop up so frequently that it is very hard for mathematics to stay pure.) From this point of view, new mathematics is important because it is more fundamental and basic; no real understanding of any mathematics, from arithmetic to calculus and beyond, is possible without it.

Many individuals, committees, and institutions have suggested programs designed to rejuvenate school mathematics. One symptom of their modernity is their predilection for initials; the very names of most suggest an esoteric unknowability. For the benefit of the uninitiated, here is a short list of some of these new programs, with translations. The order is roughly chronological.

UICSM. The University of Illinois Committee on School Mathematics, directed by Dr. Max Beberman.

APP of CEEB. The Advanced Placement Program of the College Entrance Examination Board. Besides stressing new mathematical concepts, this program outlines an accelerated course for students who are capable of completing a year of college mathematics in high school.

CUPM. The Committee on the Undergraduate Program in Mathematics of the Mathematical Association of America, concerned with the curriculum in colleges and universities.

The Commission. The commission on mathematics of the College Entrance Examination Board. This group completed its work in 1959 by issuing a report containing detailed outlines of its recommended courses and appendices clarifying and expanding some topics. It has been very influential, partly because the College Entrance Examination Board can and does include in its testing program any topics it considers important.

Ball State Teachers College Experimental Program, directed for most of its life by Dr. Charles Brumfiel and tried out at Burris, the Ball State Laboratory School.

The Madison Project, started at Madison Junior High School, Madison, Wisconsin by Dr. Robert Davis of Syracuse University.

UMMaP. The University of Maryland Mathematics Project.

Boston College Mathematical Series, directed by the Rev. Stanley Bezuszka.

SMSG. The School Mathematics Study Group. This very influential group, with headquarters originally at Yale and now at Stanford, has produced sample textbooks and teachers' manuals for many courses, elementary and advanced.

Algebra for grade 5, originated by Dr. W. W. Sawyer of Wesleyan University, and now extended to other grades.

SSCC or NCTM-SSCC. Secondary School Curriculum Committee of the National Council of Teachers of Mathematics. Besides making detailed recommendations for various grade levels, this group has studied European mathematics education and contrasted it with our programs.

All of these programs and others not mentioned here agree in certain essentials. They stress underlying concepts, structure, and logic, rather than intricate manipulations, complicated calculations, and rote learning. Wherever possible, students are encouraged to discover patterns and relationships for themselves. Mathematics is becoming an exciting challenge, not only for the scientific wizard but even for the average student.

The people who make up tests are keeping pace with the changes in mathematics teaching and even setting the pace in some respects. Here are some sample items from the College Entrance Examination Board, problems of the sort that this organization considers important. They show the sort of thinking stressed in the new programs and they illustrate the types of questions students nowadays can expect to meet on mathematics examinations.

1. If there are 400 students in a school, which of the following statements is (are) true?
   I. There must be at least one month in which 30 or more students have a birthday anniversary.
   II. Some students must have birthday anniversaries on the same day.
   III. Some students must have been born in the same year and on the same day.
   (A) I only   (B) II only   (C) III only   (D) I and II only   (E) I, II, and III

2. Two variables in a scientific experiment are such that their product is always 1. If, for a certain time, one variable is greater than zero, less than 1, and decreasing, then which of the following best describes the second variable?
   (A) Greater than 1 and increasing
   (B) Greater than 1 and decreasing
   (C) Not changing
   (D) Less than 1 and increasing
   (E) Less than 1 and decreasing

3. If x, y, z, and w are all real numbers and none of them is zero, which of the following expressions can equal zero?
   I. $x + y + z + w$
   II. $x^2 + y^2 + z^2 + w^2$
   III. $x^3 + y^3 + z^3 + w^3$
   IV. $x^4 + y^4 + z^4 + w^4$
   (A) I only   (B) III only   (C) II and IV only
   (D) I and III only   (E) I, II, III, and IV

4. If $x(x - y) = 0$ and if y does not equal zero, which of the following is true?
   (A) $x = 0$ (B) Either $x = 0$ or $x = y$ (C) $x = y$
   (D) $x^2 = y$ (E) Both $x = 0$ and $x - y = 0$

5. Of three coins, Q, R, and S, two are counterfeit. One counterfeit weighs more than the good coin, while the other weighs less. Q proves to be heavier than R when weighed. Which of the following statements is true?
   (A) Q and S are counterfeit.
   (B) R and S are counterfeit.
   (C) Q and R are counterfeit.
   (D) Q or R but not both are counterfeit.
   (E) Q or R or both are counterfeit.

6. If ϕ is an operation on the positive numbers, for which of the following definitions of ϕ is $x \phi y = y \phi x$?
   (A) $x \phi y = \dfrac{x}{y}$
   (B) $x \phi y = x - y$
   (C) $x \phi y = x(x + y)$
   (D) $x \phi y = \dfrac{xy}{x + y}$
   (E) $x \phi y = x^2 + xy^2 + y^4$

7. Which of the following properties is (are) applicable to both the set of integers and the set of rational numbers?
   I. Between any two of the set there is a third.
   II. There is a least positive number of the set.
   III. There is a greatest number of the set.
   (A) None   (B) I only   (C) II only   (D) III only
   (E) II and III only

8. The symbol $\cap$ represents the intersection of two sets and the symbol $\cup$ represents the union of two sets. Which of the following represents the shaded portion of the Venn diagram?

   (A) $(X \cap Y) \cup Z$
   (B) $X \cup (Y \cap Z)$
   (C) $X \cap (Y \cup Z)$
   (D) $(X \cap Y) \cap Z$
   (E) $(X \cup Y) \cap Z$

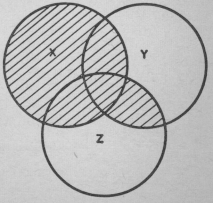

9. How many numbers in the set $\{-5, -3, 0, 3\}$ satisfy both of the conditions $|n - 3| \leq 6$, and $|n + 2| < 5$?
   (A) None   (B) One   (C) Two   (D) Three   (E) Four

10. The number of points in the intersection of the graph of $x = y$ and the graph of $|x| + |y| = 1$ is
   (A) None   (B) One   (C) Two   (D) Three
   (E) Four

ANSWERS: 1. B   2. A   3. D   4. B   5. E
         6. D   7. A   8. B   9. C   10. C

By the time you finish this book, you, too, should understand the problems.

Since in this country everybody studies some mathematics, it is inevitable that many students are learning the "new" mathematics and coming home to confound their parents with it. The number of bewildered adults is legion, and the resulting furor has even invaded magazines and newspapers. The *Chicago Tribune Magazine* printed a series of articles entitled "The New Math" in 1962 ("'I just LOVE the commutative law for addition,' purrs one curly-topped first grader"). The *Saturday Review* (January 19, 1963) contained an article "The New Math: You Don't Count on Your Fingers Any More," and *The Christian Science Monitor* at about the same time started a series of ten articles on modern mathematics ("Socrates Would Have Taught 'New' Math," says one headline). *The New York Times* and the *Atlantic Monthly*, among others, have gotten into the act with their versions.

Well, what *is* it all about? This book is an attempt to explain.

Chapter 3
In the Beginning

New trends in elementary-school mathematics are more in method than in content. However, topics that used to be reserved for high-school courses are started in a simple and intuitive way in some elementary-school programs.

If you visit an arithmetic class and find it very different from what it used to be, it might be because of the teaching, it might be because of the subject matter, and it might be because of the general classroom atmosphere. In an elementary-school class where "new math" is being taught, it's likely to be some of all three.

There have always been some excellent arithmetic teachers in elementary schools. They know and like their subject, they know and like kids, and they know how to bring the two together. There have also been the other kind—teachers who had no particular interest in arithmetic, whose training in mathematics was minimal, and who felt safe only if they stuck to tradition as far as numbers were concerned. Elementary-school teachers have to be jacks-of-all-trades. It was rare that there was a specialist in arithmetic among them. A few years ago you could seldom find anybody who was willing to try something new in elementary school mathematics.

Today things have changed. High-school and college mathematics teachers have become more interested in the elementary schools and have gone into them. Sometimes they have taught classes, sometimes they have helped the teachers understand the foundations of arithmetic better, and often they have done both. Besides, many publishers have brought out new and up-to-date books and materials with detailed teachers' manuals. (One of these is Robert Wirtz and Morton Botel's *Math Workshop for Children*, which contains some of the material in this chapter.) SMSG (School Mathematics Study Group) now has books prepared for the upper grades of elementary school. Seminars and summer schools have helped teachers inform and orient themselves. (It should encourage perplexed parents to know that teachers had to go back to school to learn the new math.)

Much of the change in elementary schools has been an improvement in the methods of teaching arithmetic rather than a change in content. It's not the mathematics that's new; it's the approach. The teacher does less explaining and expounding, and the children do more exploring and inventing. Of course, good teachers have always used the natural curiosity of the children and encouraged them to find things out for themselves.

Seeing Number Relationships

We no longer present children with a lot of addition combinations or an addition table to memorize. They make their own. Counting groups of objects leads to the facts of addition.

This illustration
should suggest that

$$3 + 2 = 5$$

After many such experiences with pictures, pencils, toys, coins, and the like, the class can summarize what they have found in a table—a small one at first:

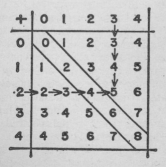

+	0	1	2	3	4
0	0	1	2	3	4
1	1	2	3	4	5
2	2	3	4	5	6
3	3	4	5	6	7
4	4	5	6	7	8

What can we see in it? For one thing, the two sides of the diagonal bar are alike: 2 + 3 is 5 in the top part—follow the arrows (1), and 3 + 2 is also 5 in the bottom part. This symmetry tells us that addition can be done in either order (for example, that 2 plus 3 is the same as 3 plus 2). This is called the *commutative law;* it holds also for multiplication. We will return to it later. Most numbers occur many times in the table: for example, there are five "4's." That means that there must be five names for "4": "0 + 4," "1 + 3," "2 + 2," "3 + 1," and "4 + 0." What can we make of the fact that odd and even numbers alternate? What other patterns are there?

Changing an odd number by 1 will always result in an even number. So if we start at any odd number in the table, we will find an even number directly above, below, left, and right. However, changing an odd number by 2 gives another odd number. So starting at an odd number in the table, we will find odd numbers diagonally above to the left and below to the right. Each diagonal from the upper right to the lower left has all along it one number, from which each step downwards adds 1 and each step to the left subtracts 1 to balance.

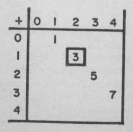

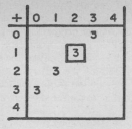

The same table can be used for subtraction. When we can add, we don't need to learn a new set of subtraction facts. The expression "7 − 3 = ?" means "find what you must add to 3 to get 7." The addition facts are sufficient to answer this.

Multiplication facts and tables can be discovered, too. If the goal is 12 units from the start, how can you make it if your footsteps are all the same size—any size you want? Bill may take 1 giant step, 12 units long; Bob takes 4 steps, 3 units long; Ann takes 6 steps, 2 units long; and so on. Some imaginative child

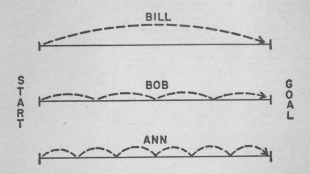

may take steps only ½ unit long, and pretty soon you're multiplying fractions, too. Of course, division is involved here as well; for "12 ÷ 2" means "find the number you must multiply by 2 to get 12." As one pupil said, "Division problems are just sneaky ways of finding how much we know about multiplication."

Blocks, sticks, the abacus, and other objects have often been used in teaching arithmetic to give children a concrete picture of what is meant by the abstract idea of a number. Now we have

"They've changed the arithmetic books since my day. The way
Junior explains it, I'm learning something."

various new materials and ingenious ways of using them. One of the best known of these is the *Cuisenaire rods*. These are sets of wooden sticks in ten different lengths and colors. There are white ones 1 unit long, red ones 2 units long, light-green ones 3 units long, and so on up to orange ones 10 units long. By matching lengths, the children find out what combinations add to 10 units (or any other number), how many light-green sticks are needed to match in length an orange and red together, and other arithmetic facts involving the four fundamental operations. Fractions come in early and naturally. Often children learn the facts before they know the names and symbols for the numbers. They may know that two light-green rods together equal a dark-green one before they know the words and symbols for the words *three* and *six*.

Children find from using the rods how numbers larger than 10 are built up; for instance, by using four orange rods and two whites, they can build the number 42. They can also see that the same scheme could be used with rods of other lengths. If they don't want to use the orange ones, they can use the blue 9-unit ones to build a large number by having several blues and some whites just as well. This leads to the idea of constructing numbers based on groups of ten or of any other number. We generally think in tens; that is, ten is the *base* of our number system. Children can just as easily think of numbers constructed with some other base. (We will return to this concept in the next chapter.)

Through Cuisenaire rods and similar devices, abstract ideas are given concrete representation. With them, teachers can show not only the facts of addition, subtraction, multiplication, and division but also the structure of the number system. They are teaching not arithmetic but mathematics.

Patterns in Pictures

Looking for patterns in tables and in diagrams can be exciting. What do we get if we write all the numbers from 0 to 100, in rows of ten, and then color every third square? every seventh? Why do the pictures look so different? (W. W. Sawyer has called this approach "Wall Paper Arithmetic.") Making such a diagram should convince anyone that multiplication is repeated addition. For example, in Figure 2, as we continue to count seven squares over, we go from 0 to 7 to 14 to 21 and so on, getting all the

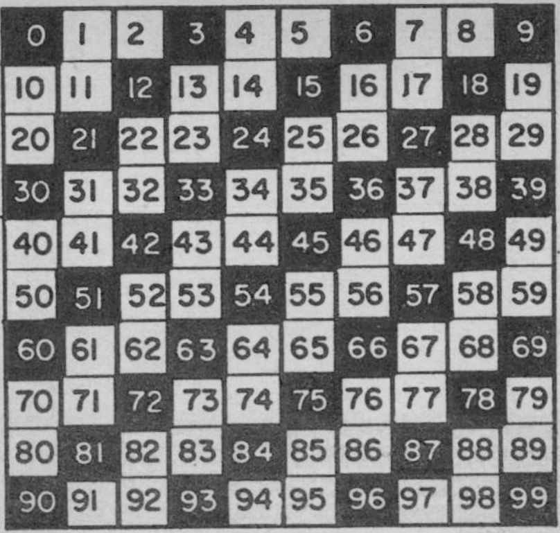

Figure 1

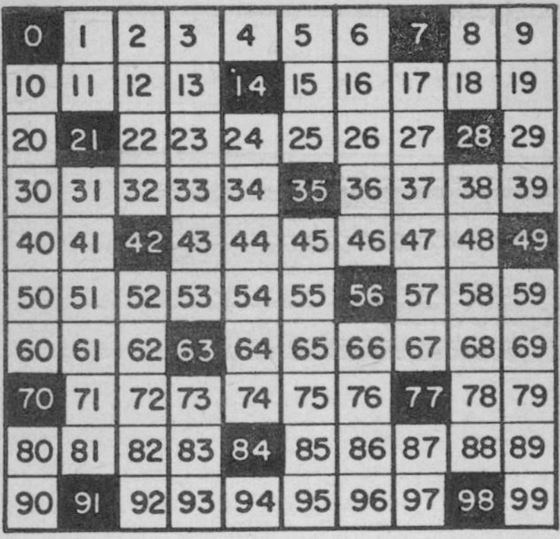

Figure 2

multiples of 7. The patterns resulting from using different numbers vary; for instance, using 5 gives a very uninteresting design, while 6 makes a simple, rather pleasing one.

Another pattern for addition shows how many names can be found for any number. Figure 3 shows 12 as the sum of six pairs of numbers, and of course there are more. With such a picture, children can hardly fail to discover negative numbers for themselves: suppose we start one of the dotted lines higher up, at "15" on the left line in Figure 4, for instance?

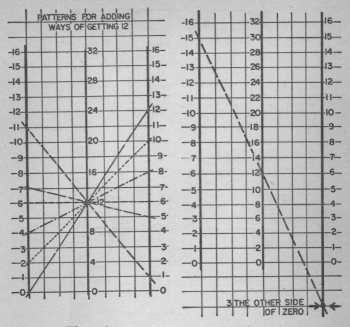

Figure 3   Figure 4

Have you ever seen a "cross-number puzzle"? A simple one appears below. Put any four numbers in the center squares, and then fill in the border with the sum of the two numbers in that row, column, or diagonal. Thus the square marked *A* is 4 because $1 + 3 = 4$; *B*, as well as *A*, is 4 because $3 + 1 = 4$.

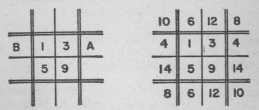

What patterns are here now? Why are the opposite ends of each line (row, column, and diagonal)* the same? Because the sum of two numbers is the same regardless of the order in

*A *row* is horizontal. A *column* is vertical. A *diagonal* is slantwise.

which we take them. This is the commutative law for addition again. The same reason holds throughout.

Notice also that the four corners add to 36, and the other border numbers add to 72, exactly twice as much. Is this an accident? Hardly. The four corners are the sums of each diagonal taken twice, that is, $1 + 9$, $9 + 1$, $5 + 3$, and $3 + 5$. Thus, 36 is twice the sum of the four numbers we started with. The other border numbers are the sums of each row (1 and 3, 5 and 9), and each column (1 and 5, 3 and 9) taken twice. So, since each of the original numbers is in both a row and a column, 72 is four times the sum of those numbers. Naturally, the second result must be twice the first. Moreover, $6 + 12$ and $4 + 14$ and $10 + 8$ are all the same.

Why?

> $6 + 12$ is the sum of the numbers in the columns.
>
> $4 + 14$ is the sum of the numbers in the rows.
>
> $10 + 8$ is the sum of the numbers in the diagonals.

Each is 18, the sum of the four numbers we started with. Try it with four other numbers in the center squares.

A cross-number puzzle can be used to develop the idea of *carrying* in adding. For instance, $68 + 27$ can be thought of as $(60 + 8) + (20 + 7)$, and the arrangement in the figure below can be used.

60	8	68
20	7	27
80	15	95

Pictures can often clear up relations and answer questions for us. For example, what does "4^2" mean? We read it "four squared" and it means "4×4." We can picture it as

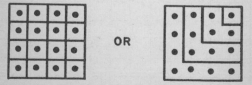

OR

If we divide it up as shown, we see that $4^2 = 1 + 3 + 5 + 7$, the sum of the first four odd numbers. Does this pattern work for other square numbers? Try it for 3^2 or 5^2. Are these, too, the sums of consecutive odd numbers? Yes. For example, $3^2 = 9$ and $9 = 1 + 3 + 5$, and $5^2 = 25$ and $25 = 1 + 3 + 5 + 7 + 9$.

Is $(3 + 2)^2$ the same as $3^2 + 2^2$? No; since, if we put together

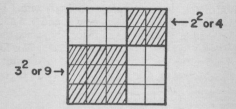

3^2 and 2^2, we don't get 5^2. Two groups of six small squares each must be put in to fill out the large square that represents 5^2 or 25. (There is a persistent delusion among high-school and even college students that $(x + y)^2$ is the same as $x^2 + y^2$; a diagram like this might dispose of it.) Can we generalize? How does

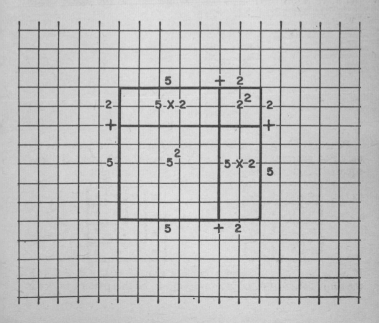

$(5 + 2)^2$ compare with $5^2 + 2^2$? They are unequal; $(5 + 2)^2 = 5^2 + 2^2 + 2(5 \times 2)$. A square whose side is $5 + 2$, or 7, can be broken up into two squares whose sides are 5 and 2, respectively, and two rectangles each with dimensions 5 and 2.

Another example: Without a lot of work, can we find $1 + 2 + 3 + 4 + 5$? or $1 + 2 + 3 + 4 + \cdots + 17 + 18 + 19 + 20$? (The dots mean to continue the pattern.) With a picture, it's not too hard. Here is $1 + 2 + 3$.

If we put another figure just like it next to itself, we get

which is easy to find. This is 3×4 or 12, so $1 + 2 + 3$ is $\frac{1}{2}$ of 12, or is 6. Here is twice $1 + 2 + 3 + 4 + 5$, which is 5×6, or 30.

So, $1 + 2 + 3 + 4 + 5$ is $\frac{1}{2} (5 \times 6)$, or 15. We can see from the diagram that the rectangle formed is 1 unit longer than it is wide. From the pattern $1 + 2 + 3 + 4 + \cdots + 17 + 18 + 19 + 20$ must be $\frac{1}{2} (20 \times 21)$, or 210. Can you find the sum of all the numbers from 1 to 100?*

*It is $\frac{1}{2} (100 \times 101)$, or 5050.

Is It Algebra or Arithmetic?

"He was a president of the United States." True or false? Of course, you can't tell unless you know who "he" is. There are 35 replacements for "he" that will make the sentence true and many more that will make it false. If we had said, "He was president of the United States in 1862," only one replacement would make it true.

A sentence like this, that is either true or false depending on the meaning attached to a certain word, is called an *open sentence*. The word that needs clarifying is usually a pronoun. By analogy, some people use the word *pronumeral* to mean something that represents a numeral. Others call it a *place-holder*, or a *variable*. It is usually indicated by a frame of some shape.

$$\square + 3 = 8$$

is an open sentence in arithmetic. If "$\square$" represents "5," it is true. If it represents any other number, it is false.

This leads to the sort of thinking we used to do in algebra; then, we wrote

$$x + 3 = 8$$

and called it *solving an equation.*

Letting letters stand for numbers is somewhat abstract for young children. They are too busy learning the primary use of letters to think of them as numbers as well. The frames seem to work very nicely. They challenge the child to find the number or numbers that make an open sentence true.

If the same-shaped frame is used more than once, the same number must fit in it each time. Different-shaped frames may have different numbers.

In how many ways can we make this open statement true?

$$\square + \triangle = 7$$

By the time children have found eight ways, they have learned eight addition facts and the subtraction facts that go with them. What numbers will make

$$\square + \square = 2 \times \square$$

correct? Many different replacements will probably be suggested. When we find that any number works (remember the same number must go in each of the three frames), we decide that this is an *identity*, true for all replacements.

Another identity is

$$\Delta + \square = \square + \Delta$$

We don't find the teacher announcing this. Instead, we find the class trying one pair of numbers after another until they come to that conclusion.

$$\square + \square + \square = 1$$

Only one replacement will do here ($\frac{1}{3}$); we may not know its name at first or the symbol to use in writing it, but in this way we soon discover fractions.

$$\square + \Delta - \square = 4$$

This presents a new pattern. We find that any number may go in the $\square$'s, but only the number four may go in the Δ. Why should this happen? Because $\square - \square = 0$ for any $\square$, so $\square + \Delta - \square$ is the same as Δ.

By the fourth grade, children can discover replacements for quite difficult open sentences. For instance, they would substitute either 2 or 11 for the frames in

$$(\square \times \square) - (13 \times \square) + 22 = 0 \qquad (1)$$

and either 3 or 4 for the frames in

$$(\square \times \square) - (7 \times \square) + 12 = 0 \qquad (2)$$

Using 2, the left side of the first equation becomes $4 - 26 + 22$, which does equal zero. Using 11, it reads $121 - 143 + 22 = 0$. The second equation with 3 in lieu of the frames reads $9 - 21 + 12 = 0$. With 4, it reads $16 - 28 + 12 = 0$.

In high school the children will meet similar open sentences, but the sentences will contain letters rather than frames. But how do they find the solutions in the fourth grade? Curiosity works wonders. Of course, they experiment. They find many numbers that don't work and—finally—a couple that do. After working through eight or ten such problems, maybe some bright youngster will look for a *pattern*.

The first problem had the numbers 13 and 22 in it, and 2 and 11 were suitable replacements. The second problem had 7 and 12, and 3 and 4 were the solutions. Any pattern here? Someone may see that

$$2 \mid 11 = 13 \quad \text{and} \quad 2 \times 11 = 22$$
$$3 + 4 = 7 \quad \text{and} \quad 3 \times 4 = 12$$

We wonder if this will work for other such problems. What about $(\square \times \square) - (6 \times \square) + 8 = 0$? Sure enough, 2 works and so does 4. $4 + 2 = 6$ and $4 \times 2 = 8$; using 4, $16 - 24 + 8 = 0$ and, using 2, $4 - 12 + 8 = 0$.

PROBLEMS

(These problems are from a workbook called *Discovery in Algebra!* It was developed in the Madison Project and was quoted in *The Christian Science Monitor*, January 12, 1963.)

Which of these statements are identities?

1. $3 \times \square = \square \times 3$
2. $131 \times \square = \square \times 131$
3. $\square \times 0 = \square$
4. $\square \times 1 = 1$
5. $\square + 0 = \square$
6. $\square \times 2 = 2$
7. $(\square \times \square) - (5 \times \square) + 6 = 0$
8. $\square \div \square = 1$
9. $\square \times 1 = \square$
10. $\square = \square$
11. $\square + \square + \square = 3 \times \square$
12. $(\square + 3) \times (\square + 3) = (\square \times \square) + (6 \times \square) + 9$

ANSWERS AND EXPLANATIONS

Statements 1, 2, 5, 8, 9, 10, 11, and 12 are identities; any number you put in the frame makes them true. (In statement 8, zero cannot be used; see page 75.) The others are not; they can be made true or false. To make them true, the replacements should be: (3) 0   (4) 1   (6) 1   (7) 3 or 2

Geometry, Too

Children experiment and discover simple geometric facts as well as arithmetic ones. How many times can two straight lines meet? Everyone tries to find as many intersections as he can. Why can't we use this diagram and decide they can meet twice?

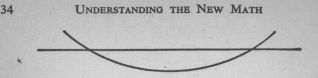

(*Answer:* One of the lines is not straight.) After coming to a conclusion here, we try three straight lines, then four. Experiment, discover, work it out for yourself. (*Answer:* 3 lines, 3 places; 4 lines, 6 places.)

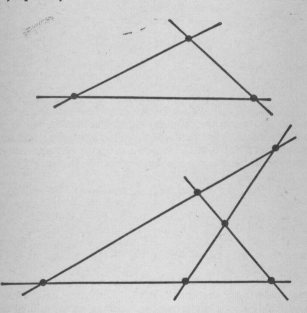

Discovery is the important word here. Try it, look for a pattern, test your pattern, and extend it if you can.

Some of the topics you find discussed in this and later chapters are taught in the elementary grades in some schools. However, whether the content is new or old, the spirit and approach are new. We no longer have arithmetic as long lists of drill exercises. We have mathematical thinking. The drill is there, concealed, and motivated by experimenting, looking for plausible inferences, and checking and verifying the inferences. Children are interested, excited, and challenged. It's not necessarily new math that does it; it's good teaching.

SECTION II
Arithmetic and Algebra

We are used to saying that something is "as sure as 1 and 1 are 2." It is probably very upsetting to see statements, from responsible mathematical sources, that "1 + 1 = 10," or "1 + 1 = 0," or "1 + 1 = 1." (You will find all these somewhere in this book.) Do mathematicians say things like this merely in order to shake our faith in the fundamentals of arithmetic and human knowledge? Not quite. Numerals are symbols, and no statements using them can be understood unless we know just what the symbols stand for.

Most of us are not used to Roman numerals. So when we see something like MCMLXXXVI, for example, we are very aware that it is an intricate symbol that has to be translated into an understandable form: 1986. However, when you get right down to it, "1986" is every bit as complicated a symbol—we just happen to be more familiar with Arabic numerals than we are with Roman numerals.

When we write two letters together in algebra, we *know* we are multiplying them; *ab* means "*a* times *b*." When we write a fraction immediately after a whole number, we *know* we are adding them; $3\frac{1}{2}$ means "3 plus $\frac{1}{2}$." Do we *know* exactly what we mean when we write two digits together? The numeral 23 does *not* mean either "2 times 3" or "2 plus 3," but something much more complex, "2 *tens* plus 3." To get a clearer understanding of the meaning of the symbols used as Arabic numerals, we will look more closely into the way they are constructed. Let's examine the role of the "ten" in that expression and see what happens if we use other numbers instead (Chapter 4).

Using other numbers in place of the "ten" makes arithmetic look very unfamiliar. However, all the same ideas and numerical relationships are there. Only the symbols are changed. We can get a really different arithmetic (called *modular arithmetic*) by still different interpretations of the symbols (Chapter 6). Experimenting with such a system should give us greater flexibility in thinking and more understanding of our ordinary arithmetic.

Besides getting our symbols clear, we must also clarify the ideas for which they stand. The word *number* is very hard to define, but we have to know what concepts are included in it. In other words, the numbers that we need for counting are not the same as those we need for measuring. The numbers in the following list are all of different kinds and of increasing complexity:

$$5, 0, -3, 4\tfrac{1}{2}, \sqrt{2}, \sqrt{-1}$$

(The symbol $\sqrt{\ }$ means "the square root of," or asks "what number when multiplied by itself will equal the number beneath the $\sqrt{\ }$?")
Let's think about four numbers:

$$-3, 4\tfrac{1}{2}, \sqrt{2}, -\sqrt{2}$$

If we ask what is the number of boys in the room, none of the four numbers gives an acceptable answer. If we want to know the number of dozens of eggs the Jones family ate last month, $4\tfrac{1}{2}$ is the only one of the four that could be used. If I want to express the number of dollars in my bank account, -3 (representing the fact that I am overdrawn) and $4\tfrac{1}{2}$ are suitable answers, but $\sqrt{2}$ and $-\sqrt{2}$ are not. If we are representing the distance of a point on a line to the right of some fixed point, all four numbers are sensible.

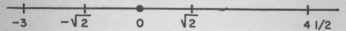

In Chapters 5 and 7, we will look at these various kinds of numbers in more detail.

Arithmetic and algebra now seem to be inextricably intertwined. Arithmetic is concerned with numbers; algebra, with variables represented by letters. But, since the letters often stand for numbers and always behave in the same way as numbers, this difference is not very significant.

A few years ago I was trying to induct a class into the mysteries of algebra by warily insinuating the idea of a formula. The ordinary simple formulas like $A = lw$ for the area of a rectangle and $p = 4s$ for the perimeter of a square aroused no particular interest or enthusiasm. Then, one of the students came up with $e = mc^2$ (Einstein's equation about the conversion of mass into energy), and I found that they all knew what a formula was. The notion of letters standing for numbers was very easy after that. Either because of atomic energy or, more probably, because formulas are now used more often in elementary schools, there seems to be no natural dividing line between algebra and arithmetic. Both deal with the way these symbols (letters or numbers) behave.

Using letters makes it easy to generalize. Instead of saying "$3 + 4 = 4 + 3$" and "$5 + 11 = 11 + 5$" and so on for many pairs of numbers, or even "$\square + \triangle = \triangle + \square$," it is simpler to say "$a + b = b + a$." In discussing arithmetic and algebraic laws, we usually use algebraic notation; that is, we use letters rather than numbers or frames.

The basic assumptions underlying algebra and arithmetic are the same. There are not very many fundamental ones, and all manipulations, calculations, and solutions of equations depend on them. These essential laws are called *axioms* or *postulates*. We have already met one, the commutative law for addition $(a + b = b + a)$. We will look at the others in Chapter 5.

If we formulate these basic laws and state them explicitly, all arithmetic and algebra is contained therein. We don't have to keep bringing in new rules every time we meet a new problem. Although it is not always easy to see how to apply the axioms in a new situation, it can always be done. Traditionally, we thought of proving theorems as being a part of geometry. This is because historically the idea of deductive reasoning was applied to geometry long ago by the ancient Greeks, and it has been part of geometry ever since. However, proofs are just as essential in algebra. There are many algebraic theorems, and their proofs are in general easier than those of geometric ones.

Both algebra and arithmetic are now less concerned than they used to be with mechanical manipulation of numbers and symbols and more concerned with the underlying meanings and reasons. This does not mean that students are not going to learn how to compute. It means merely that they should eventually compute with more speed and accuracy because they will know what they are doing and why it works.

Chapter 4

The Nature of Numbers and Numerals

The value of a numeral depends not only on its digits but also on the positions they occupy and on the base of the system. Normally we use the decimal system, based on counting by tens and powers of ten. It helps us understand the workings of this system if we study others. We can write numbers with bases other than ten and compute with them. The binary system, with a base of two, turns out to be useful in the design of computers.

Maybe the title of this chapter is confusing. Aren't numbers and numerals the same? The answer is that possibly they used to be, or, at least, when we went to school we thought they were, but they aren't any more. A *numeral* is a symbol that represents a number. A *number* is an abstract idea. For instance, "2," "II," and "β'" are the Arabic, Roman, and Greek numerals for two. *Two* is that property that twins, a couple of peas in a pod, a brace of pheasants, a yoke of oxen, a pair of pistols, and the singers of a duet have in common.

By confusing numbers and numerals, we can arrive at some very curious results. The old Romans could have had no trouble with five and ten. The number five (V) is half the number ten (X), and the numeral (symbol) "V" is also half the numeral "X," the top half. However, the numeral "IV" is larger than the numeral "V," just as in our system of Arabic numerals ".318" is larger than "7." If you're not convinced, just measure the space each of them occupies. Is 3 one half of 8, and is 8 one half of 13? No, but as in Figure 1 on page 39 the numeral "3" is one half of "8," the right half, and "VIII" is one half of "XIII."

The purpose of introducing this distinction is not so that we can make up some pointless paradoxes like these, but so that we can see that a number can be expressed in many ways. Different numerals can stand for the same number. Even without resorting to

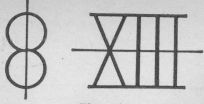

Figure 1

Roman or Greek numerals, we can still represent one number by many symbols. For instance, "$1\frac{1}{2}$," "1.5," "$\frac{6}{4}$," "$\frac{15}{10}$," and "$\frac{75}{50}$" all indicate the same number. In fact, for any point on the slanting line OP in the diagram, the ratio of its distance from the hori-

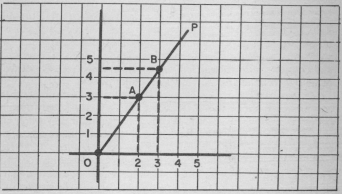

zontal line to its distance from the vertical line represents the same number. For point A, the distances are 3 and 2. For B, they are $4\frac{1}{2}$ and 3. Both $\frac{3}{2}$ and $\frac{4\frac{1}{2}}{3}$ are equal to $1\frac{1}{2}$. One point on the line must be excluded, point O. Do you see why? For point O, both distances are zero, and the ratio of zero to zero is meaningless.

The Base of a Number System

What does "10" mean? Usually, of course, it means ten, but this depends on our system for expressing numbers. We are used to a system in which the value of a *digit** depends on its location in the numeral. A sole "2" means two, but the "2" in "27" means

---

*A *digit* is a numeral used to denote a number of varying values like the "3's" in "33."

twenty. Each of the "6's" in "6666.6" has a different value, as we recognize when we read this numeral as "six *thousand*, six *hundred*, six*ty*-six and six *tenths*." Of course, "six*ty*" means six *tens*. This system is based on ten. One hundred is 10^2 (ten squared or ten times ten). One thousand is 10^3 (ten cubed or ten times ten times ten).

Why is ten so important? Why should it, of all numbers, be singled out as the base of our system of numerals? For the same reason that we use the word *digit* to stand for the separate symbols. The Latin word *digitus* means "finger" (or "toe"). We have ten fingers, and primitive men learned to count on their fingers.

There are indications that numbers other than ten were used as bases by early peoples. Some must have used their toes as well as their fingers, so that there are traces of counting by twenties. We speak of a *score*, meaning "a unit of twenty"; and the French say *soixante-dix* and *quatre-vingts* ("sixty and ten" and "four twenties") for seventy and eighty.

Commonly used fractions like thirds cannot be expressed in tenths or in twentieths. Possibly this is why bases like twelve and sixty have often been used. Thus we have 12 inches in a foot, 12 items in a dozen, 12 dozen in a gross, 12 pence in a shilling, 60 seconds in a minute, 60 minutes in an hour, and 60 minutes of angular measure in a degree. One-third of a dollar, one-quarter of a dime, and five-sixths of a meter are awkward to deal with; but one-third of a shilling, one-quarter of an hour, and five-sixths of a foot are easy.

Do we really understand what the digits mean when we write a numeral? If we do, we can write numerals with bases other than ten and understand what we are doing. The pattern and the structure do not change, whether we use ten or four or any other number as a base. The last digit tells us the number of units. This has nothing to do with the base except that it must always be less than the base.

The next-to-last digit indicates how many times the base itself is to be taken. For example, the numeral "10" usually means 1 ten, but if the base were four, it would mean 1 four. Thus "10" always means the base itself. By the same token, the numeral "30" usually means 3 tens, but if the base were four, it would mean 3 fours.

Let's consider the numeral "13." Just as

1   +   3

means "13" in base ten, or thirteen, so

means "13" in the base four, or seven. Likewise

means "13" in base five, or eight.

Let's consider the symbol "23." In base ten, it means

or twenty-three. In base four, it means

or eleven. In base five, it means

or thirteen.

The third digit from the end tells us how many times we take the square of the base (the base multiplied by itself). The numeral "200" usually means 2 hundreds (as one hundred is ten-squared). If the base were five, however, it would mean 2 twenty-fives (since twenty-five is five-squared), or fifty. Let's look at a three-digit number in base four:

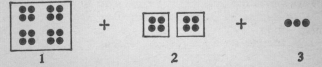

The symbol "123" means 1 four-squared (sixteen) plus 2 fours (eight) plus 3 ones (three), or twenty-seven.

The fourth digit from the end indicates how many times we have the cube of the base, and so on.

The first digit after a period indicates the number to be divided by the base. For example, ".4" usually means 4 tenths, but if six were the base, it would mean 4 sixths. The next digit shows the number to be divided by the square of the base. For example, ".02" usually means 2 hundredths, but if seven were the base, it would mean 2 forty-ninths (since seven-squared is forty-nine).

Notice that we have no digit representing the base itself or any larger number. The base itself and all numbers larger than the base must be written with two or more digits. If the base were two, our only digits would be 0 and 1; the digit "2" could not exist in this system. *Two* would be written "10." Remember that

the symbol "10" always represents the base, since "1" in the next-to-last column indicates the base taken once. For example, "63" could not be a numeral in any system with a base smaller than 7, since "6" does not exist in a system with a smaller base. If six is the base, the number six is written as "10."

Normally, we assume that all the numerals we write have ten as a base. Thus "10" means ten; ".3" means three tenths; "234" means two hundred thirty-four, that is, $200 + 30 + 4$, or $(2 \times 10^2) + (3 \times 10) + 4$, and so on. We need ten digits to express any number, symbols for the nine integers from one to nine, and zero. Zero is an essential idea in any system in which digits have place value. Without zero there would be no way of showing that the "2" in "203" means something different from the "2" in "23." When we get to the base itself, ten, we need two digits. We never have a single digit for the base.

Suppose we were to use some base other than ten; what would the same numerals signify? Let's try twelve. Now, the symbol "10" means twelve (1 dozen and no units); the symbol " ?" means two twelfths; the symbol "234" means 2 gross, 3 dozen, and 4 units ($[2 \times 12^2] + [3 \times 12] + 4$). In base twelve "234" is thus the same as "328" in base ten, since $288 + 36 + 4 = 328$ (in base ten).

234 in base twelve =

$$
\left.
\begin{array}{l}
\downarrow \text{4 units, or } 4 \times 1 \text{ or } \ldots \ldots \ldots \quad 4 \\
\downarrow \text{3} \times \text{the base, or } 3 \times 12, \text{ or } \ldots \ldots \quad 36 \\
\text{2} \times \text{the square of the base, or} \\
\quad 2 \times 12^2, 2 \times 144, \text{ or } \ldots \ldots \ldots \quad 288 \\
\hline
 328
\end{array}
\right\} \text{ in base ten}
$$

We now need twelve digits to express any number. Let us use the ten we now have, plus "X" to stand for ten and "Y" for eleven. (Different books use other symbols; some use "t" for ten and "e" for eleven; others use signs like *, ‡, etc.)

Now we count, "1, 2, 3, 4, 5, 6, 7, 8, 9, X, Y, 10, 11, 12, . . . 19, 1X, 1Y, 20, 21, . . . 29, 2X, 2Y, 30, . . ." and so on. "1X" means 1 dozen and ten, or twenty-two; "20" means two dozen or twenty-four, "2X" means 2 dozen and ten, or thirty-four. By the time we reach "100," we have 1 gross or 1 dozen dozen or one hundred forty-four. The preceding numeral is "YY," eleven dozen and eleven. By the way, don't read "100" as "one hundred." In the absence of a suitable vocabulary, "100" has to be read as "one-zero-zero."

If "100" can mean one hundred, or one gross, or other numbers depending upon the number we choose as our base, how will we ever know what we are writing? Of course, "3Y" can't mean any number with base ten, since it uses a digit, Y, not in that system. What about "217" and similar numerals? We agree to use a sub-script* to indicate what the base is whenever it is not ten, or even when it is, if we want to be sure it is clear. However, the subscript itself is a numeral. What will it mean? If we write "217_{12}," in what base is the "12"? To avoid compounding confusion, let us agree that the subscript itself will always be in the base-ten system.

Thus, "217_{12}" means 2 gross plus 1 dozen plus 7.

---

*A subscript is a small numeral written after and below another to distinguish it in some way. For instance, "101_{12}" is read "one-zero-one, sub-twelve," and means "101 in base twelve" (1 times 12 times 12 — no twelves — plus 1 unit), or "one-hundred forty-five."

"217" or "217_{10}" means 2 hundred plus 1 ten plus 7 or two hundred and seventeen.

"217_8" means 2 groups of 64 (since 64 = 8^2), 1 group of 8, and 1 group of 7.

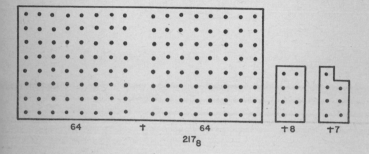

Numerals written with the base ten are said to be in the *decimal* system, those with the base twelve, in the *duodecimal* system, those with the base three, in the *ternary* system, and those with the base two, in the *binary* system. Most of the others are un-named.

Thus, $3Y_{12} = 47_{10}$ or just 47, since

$$3Y \text{ in base twelve} =$$
$$\left. \begin{array}{l} 11 \text{ units, or } 11 \times 1 \text{ or} \quad\quad 11 \\ 3 \times \text{ the base, or } 3 \times 12, \text{ or} \quad \underline{36} \\ 47 \end{array} \right\} \text{ in base ten}$$

$XOY_{12} = 1451_{10}$ or just 1451, since

$$XOY \text{ in base twelve} =$$
$$\left. \begin{array}{l} 11 \text{ units, or } 11 \times 1, \text{ or } \ldots\ldots\ldots\ldots \quad 11 \\ 0 \times \text{ the base, or } 0 \times 12, \text{ or } \ldots\ldots\ldots \quad\; 0 \\ 10 \times \text{ the square of the base, or } 10 \times 144, \text{ or } \underline{1440} \\ 1451 \end{array} \right\} \text{ in base ten}$$

To go in the other direction, from the decimal to the duodecimal system, we have to break up our numbers into grosses (144's) and dozens (12's) and units.

Thus, $307_{10} = 288 + 12 + 7 = 217_{12}$, since

$$
\begin{array}{l}
288 = 2 \times 144 = 2 \times 12^2 \\
\ 12 = \ldots\ldots\ \Big| \ \ldots 1 \times 12 \\
\ \ \ 7 = \ldots\ldots\ \Big\downarrow \ \ldots \Big\downarrow \qquad 7 \text{ units} \\
\qquad\qquad\quad 2 \qquad 1 \qquad 7 \\
\qquad\qquad\quad \underbrace{} \\
\qquad\qquad\qquad\quad 217_{12}
\end{array}
$$

$$
480_{10} = 432 + 48 + 0 = 340_{12}, \text{ since}
$$

$$
\begin{array}{l}
432 = 3 \times 144 = 3 \times 12^2 \\
\ 48 = \ldots\ldots\ \Big| \ \ldots 4 \times 12 \\
\ \ \ 0 = \ldots\ldots\ \Big\downarrow \ \ldots \Big\downarrow \qquad 0 \text{ units} \\
\qquad\qquad\quad 3 \qquad 4 \qquad 0 \\
\qquad\qquad\quad \underbrace{} \\
\qquad\qquad\qquad\quad 340_{12}
\end{array}
$$

To see what advantages and disadvantages there are in using a large or a small base, let us write 1727_{10} in both the duodecimal and the binary systems. In the *duodecimal* system, we must think

$$
\begin{aligned}
1727_{10} &= 1584 + 132 + 11 \\
&= (11 \times 144) + (11 \times 12) + 11 = YYY_{12}
\end{aligned}
$$

To write it in the *binary* system, we must think

$$
\begin{aligned}
1727_{10} &= 1024 + 512 + 128 + 32 + 16 + 8 + 4 + 2 + 1 \\
&= 2^{10} + 2^9 + 2^7 + 2^5 + 2^4 + 2^3 + 2^2 + 2 + 1 \\
&= 11,010,111,111_2
\end{aligned}
$$

The advantage of using a large number as a base is that numbers can be expressed with fewer symbols than when we use a small base. The advantage of using a small base is that only a small number of distinct digits are needed, and only a few number combinations need to be learned. For instance, in the binary system, there are only two digits, 0 and 1; and all numbers must be written using these digits only. The whole arithmetic is:

$$
\begin{array}{llll}
0 + 0 = 0 & 0 + 1 = 1 & 1 + 0 = 1 & 1 + 1 = 10 \\
0 \times 0 = 0 & 0 \times 1 = 0 & 1 \times 0 = 0 & 1 \times 1 = 1
\end{array}
$$

We shall discuss this in more detail later in the chapter.

PROBLEMS

1. Write these numbers in the decimal system:
   For example: $312_4 = (3 \times 4^2) + (1 \times 4) + 2$
   $$= (3 \times 16) + \quad 4 \quad + 2$$
   $$= \quad 48 \quad + \quad 4 \quad + 2 = 54_{10}$$
   (a) 52_{12} (b) 41_5 (c) 111_2 (d) 46_7
   (e) 202_3 (f) $.4_{12}$ (g) 2_{13} (h) 2_7

2. Write these decimal numbers in the system with five as a base:
   For example: $29 = 25 + 4 = (1 \times 5^2) + (0 \times 5) + 4 = 104_5$
   (a) 5   (b) 25   (c) 63   (d) 130
   (e) 700   (f) 124   (g) .4   (h) .04

3. Count to sixteen in the binary system.
   (*Hint:* It starts 1, 10, 11, 100, . . .)

ANSWERS AND EXPLANATIONS

1. (a) 62. $52_{12} = (5 \times 12) + 2 = 60 + 2$
   (b) 21. $41_5 = (4 \times 5) + 1 = 20 + 1$
   (c) 7. $111_2 = (1 \times 4) + (1 \times 2) + 1 = 4 + 2 + 1$
   (d) 34. $46_7 = (4 \times 7) + 6 = 28 + 6$
   (e) 20. $202_3 = (2 \times 9) + (0 \times 3) + 2 = 18 + 2$
   (f) $\frac{1}{3}$. $.4_{12} = 4$ twelfths
   (g) 2
   (h) 2

   The answers to (g) and (h) are the same because the base determines the value of digits other than that in the units place. The units digit indicates the number of units, whatever the base is.

2. (a) 10_5. $5 = (1 \times 5)$, which is 1 group of five, with no units left over, so we put "0" in the units place and place a numeral "1" in the fives place, denoting 1 group of five.
   (b) 100_5. $25 = (1 \times 5^2) + (0 \times 5) + 0$
   (c) 223_5. $63 = (2 \times 5^2) + (2 \times 5) + 3$
   (d) 1010_5. $130 = (1 \times 5^3) + (0 \times 5^2) + (1 \times 5) + 0$
   (e) 10300_5. $700 = (1 \times 5^4) + (0 \times 5^3) + (3 \times 5^2)$
   $$+ (0 \times 5) + 0$$
   (f) 444_5. $124 = (4 \times 5^2) + (4 \times 5) + 4$
   (g) $.2_5$. $.4 = \dfrac{4}{10} = \dfrac{2}{5}$
   (h) $.01_5$. $.04 = \dfrac{4}{100} = \dfrac{1}{25} = \dfrac{1}{5^2}$

3. Base 10: 1,   2,   3,   4,   5,   6,   7,   8,   9,   10,
   Base 2: 1, 10, 11, 100, 101, 110, 111, 1000, 1001, 1010,

   Base 10: 11,   12,   13,   14,   15,   16.
   Base 2: 1011, 1100, 1101, 1110, 1111, 10000.

Computing in Systems with Other Bases

Naturally, the facts of arithmetic don't change. Two plus five is *always* seven. If the symbols vary, it's because different numerals have these meanings. Here are several ways of saying the same thing:

$2 + 5 = 7$ (base 12)
$2 + 5 = 7$ (base 10)
$2 + 5 = 7$ (base 8)
$2 + 5 = 10$ (base 7; now seven is written "10")
$2 + 5 = 11$ (base 6; now "10" means six and "11" means seven)
$2 + 10 = 12$ (base 5; now "10" means five)
$2 + 11 = 13$ (base 4; now "10" means four and "11" means five)
$2 + 12 = 21$ (base 3; now "10" means three and "20" means six)
$10 + 101 = 111$ (base 2; now "10" means two)

In any system with a base larger than seven, "$2 + 5 = 7$" looks the same.

Are any of the following equations still true if the numerals are written with other bases than ten?

$$10^2 = 100$$
$$23 \times 10 = 230$$
$$6.83 \times 10 = 68.3$$
$$12 \div 100 = .12$$

Yes, all are true in any system in which these numerals can exist, since "10" always represents the base itself. To multiply a whole number by 10 (the base) in any system, we must add a 0. This has the effect of moving every digit one column to the left, which multiplies each digit and thus the number itself by the base. In a number which is not a whole number, as in the third and fourth equations above, the same thing is accomplished by shifting the period (the decimal point, if we are in the decimal system) one place to the right. To divide by 10 (the base), each digit must be shifted one column to the right by moving the period one place to the left. This divides each digit by the base, and so divides the entire number by the base likewise.

In what system is it true that $34 + 21 = 55$? In any system in which these numerals (containing the digits 0 through 5) exist— that is, in any system in which the base is six or more.

In what system is this addition problem correct?

$$\begin{array}{r} 24 \\ 53 \\ \hline 121 \end{array}$$

First, we know that $4 + 3 =$ seven. However, the numeral "7" is, obviously, not being used. Therefore the system must be one in which the digit 7 does not exist. Immediately, then, we know that the base cannot be seven or any number larger than seven. The digits 1 through 5 do, though, exist in base six. Second, the last column tells us that $4 + 3 = 1$ or some numeral ending in "1." The sum of 4 units and 3 units is not, however, 1 unit. Therefore, it must be a numeral ending in "1." If $4 + 3 = 11$, then "11" must represent seven. This is true in base six. In this case,

24 means (2×6)	$+ \quad 4$
53 means (5×6)	$+ \quad 3$
Adding, we get $\qquad (7 \times 6)$	$+ \quad 7$

Breaking it down, we get	$(7 \times 6) \quad + (6 + 1)$
or	$(7 \times 6) \quad + (\text{the base} + 1 \text{ more}$
	$\qquad\qquad\qquad \text{than the base})$
or, adding 1 group of six,	$(8 \times 6) \quad + \quad 1$

So, since 8 equals $6 + 2$, we may substitute $(6 + 2)$ for the 8 in the expression (8×6), getting

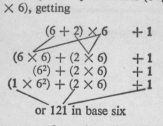

$$(6 + 2) \times 6 \qquad + 1$$
$$(6 \times 6) + (2 \times 6) \qquad + 1$$
$$(6^2) + (2 \times 6) \qquad + 1$$
or $\qquad (1 \times 6^2) + (2 \times 6) \qquad + 1$

or 121 in base six

Because we had to carry from the units column into the next column, it made a considerable difference what the base was. (In the example before this there was no carrying.) In the decimal system, we carry tens or groups of ten. In the system with base six, we carry sixes or groups of six.

Similarly, this subtraction problem, with no borrowing, is true in a system with any base greater than five.

$$\begin{array}{r} 45 \\ 32 \\ \hline 13 \end{array}$$

However, if we have this subtraction,

$$\begin{array}{r} 72 \\ 43 \\ \hline ? \end{array}$$

we must start by borrowing. If this is in the decimal system,

$$72 = \qquad (7 \times 10) \qquad + 2$$

Borrowing 1 group of ten, we get

$$72 = (6 \times 10) + (1 \times 10) + 2$$

$$72 = (6 \times 10) + \qquad (10 + 2)$$

and by combining,

$$72 = \quad 60 \qquad + \quad 12$$

Breaking 43 down, we get

$$43 = (4 \times 10) + 3$$

and

$$43 = \quad 40 \quad + 3$$

so

$$72 = 60 + 12$$

minus

$$43 = 40 + 3$$

gives us

$$\overline{29 = 20 + 9}$$

If the base for this example were eight,

$$72_8 = (7 \times 8) \qquad\qquad + \quad 2$$

or

$$(6 \times 8) + (1 + 8) + \quad 2$$

or

$$(6 \times 8) \qquad\qquad + (8 + 2)$$

Also,

$$43_8 = (4 \times 8) \qquad\qquad + \quad 3$$

So we start by computing $(8 + 2) - 3$, having borrowed eight.

Base 8   Base 10

$$72_8 = (6 \times 8) + 10$$
$$43_8 = (4 \times 8) + 3$$
$$\overline{27_8 = (2 \times 8) + 7}, \text{ or twenty-three in base ten}$$

When will computation problems look the same in different systems? If each column can be treated independently, with no carrying or borrowing, the base won't matter. However, if we have to *carry*, we must know if we are carrying ten or some other number into the next column. If we have to *borrow*, we must know if we are borrowing ten or some other number from the next column.

All of us learned the fundamental operations years ago, probably so thoroughly that the procedures became mechanical and we have no need to figure out why they work. It takes a great deal of drill and effort to arrive at this sort of mechanical perfection. If we really understand what we are doing and why our procedures work, it should be easier for us to learn. To help us compute accurately and easily in the decimal system and to understand its workings, let us try a few computations with another base, seven. First, of course, we need our addition and multiplication tables. How can we construct them? Let's try a few computations and see.

$$3 + 5 = 8 = (1 \times 7) + 1 \text{ in base ten,}$$
so $3 + 5 = 11$ in base seven.
$$6 + 6 = 12 = (1 \times 7) + 5 \text{ in base ten,}$$
so $6 + 6 = 15$ in base seven.
$$4 \times 6 = 24 = (3 \times 7) + 3 \text{ in base ten,}$$
so $4 \times 6 = 33$ in base seven.
$$5 \times 3 = 15 = (2 \times 7) + 1 \text{ in base ten,}$$
so $5 \times 3 = 21$ in base seven.

We complete the tables in the same way. (Of course, we can make the task only half as onerous by noting that $5 + 3$ is the same as $3 + 5$, that 6×4 is the same as 4×6 and so on.) Here are the results: (In the rest of this section, all numerals are in base seven unless otherwise indicated.)

Table 1—Addition₇

+	0	1	2	3	4	5	6
0	0	1	2	3	4	5	6
1	1	2	3	4	5	6	10
2	2	3	4	5	6	10	11
3	3	4	5	6	10	11	12
4	4	5	6	10	11	12	13
5	5	6	10	11	12	13	14
6	6	10	11	12	13	14	15

Table 2—Multiplication₇

×	0	1	2	3	4	5	6
0	0	0	0	0	0	0	0
1	0	1	2	3	4	5	6
2	0	2	4	6	11	13	15
3	0	3	6	12	15	21	24
4	0	4	11	15	22	26	33
5	0	5	13	21	26	34	42
6	0	6	15	24	33	42	51

According to Table 2, 4 fives are 26 and 5 fives are 34. In any system, 4 fives + 1 five should equal 5 fives. Let's try it here.

Add: 26   *Step 1:* $6 + 5 = 14$ (from Table 1). We put down the
   5   "4," representing four units, and carry "1," repre-
  34 senting 1 group of seven, into the sevens column.

        Step 2: $2 + 1 = 3$, adding 1 group of seven to the "2" already in the sevens place. Thus, $26 + 5 = 34$, as it should.

Here are a few examples worked out in base seven and checked by redoing them in base ten.

Add: 54 *Step 1:* $4 + 6 = 13$ (from Table 1). Write the "3"
     36 and carry "1", representing 1 group of seven.
    ‾‾‾
    123

> *Step 2:* $1 + 5 = 6$ and $6 + 3 = 12$ (both sums from Table 1).

Check:

Base 7		Base 10
$54 =$	$(5 \times 7) + 4 =$	$35 + 4 = 39$
$36 =$	$(3 \times 7) + 6 =$	$21 + 6 = 27$
$123 = (1 \times 7^2) + (2 \times 7) + 3 =$		$49 + 14 + 3 = 66$

To subtract, we use the facts of addition either from Table 1 or from our knowledge of the addition facts that went into making that table. For instance, to subtract 5 from 14 in base seven, we ask ourselves what number we must add to 5 to get 14.

With the table: We look for "14" in the row beginning "5." Since "14" lies in the column headed "6," we know that $5 + 6 = 14_7$.

Without the table: Since $14_7 = (1 \times 7) + 4$, or 11_{10}, and since $5 + 6 = 11_{10}$, we know that $5 + 6 = 14_7$.

Either way, since $5 + 6 = 14$, then $14 - 5 = 6$.

Suppose we want to subtract 5 from 16. The table or our knowledge of addition facts shows that no one-digit number added to 5 gives 16. Therefore we subtract the units digits (5 from 6) and then the sevens digits (0 from 1). Here is the example done in base seven and checked in base ten:

Check:

Base 7	Base 10
$16 = (1 \times 7) + 6 = 7 + 6 = 13$	
$5 = (0 \times 7) + 5 = 0 + 5 = 5$	
$11 = (1 \times 7) + 1 = 7 + 1 = 8$	

What if we need to borrow? For instance, how can we work out this computation?

Subtract: 530
          246

We cannot subtract 6 from 0 in the units column, nor 4 from 3 in the sevens column. We begin by borrowing 1 of the 3 groups of seven from the sevens column, so that we think of 530 as 5 groups of seven-squared plus 2 groups of seven plus

"10," where the "10" means seven units. Since 10 − 6 = 1, we have

Step 1:

		groups of seven-squared	groups of seven	units
530	is	5	2	10
246	is	2	4	6
		—	—	1

We have the same sort of problem in the next step: subtracting 4 from 2 in the middle column. Now we borrow 1 of the 5 groups of seven-squared, so that, instead of 5 groups of seven-squared plus 2 groups of seven, we have 4 groups of seven-squared plus "12" groups of seven. The "12" here means nine: the two we had originally and the seven that came from one seven-squared group. Since 12 − 4 = 5 and 4 − 2 = 2, we get

Steps 2 and 3:

		groups of seven-squared	groups of seven	units
530	is	4	12	10
246	is	2	4	6
		2	5	1

Therefore 530 − 246 = 251 (in base seven).

Check:

Base 7   Base 10
$$530 = (5 \times 49) + (3 \times 7) + 0 = 245 + 21 + 0 = 266$$
$$246 = (2 \times 49) + (4 \times 7) + 6 = 98 + 28 + 6 = 132$$
$$\overline{251} = (2 \times 49) + (5 \times 7) + 1 = 98 + 35 + 1 = \overline{134}$$

*Multiplying and dividing are always more difficult than adding and subtracting. The next section is really hard; so you will have to be very ambitious to work through these examples. If you don't feel that energetic, skip to page 54 or page 57.

Let's try multiplying. Here is an example that looks the same whether we think of the numerals as being written in base seven or in base ten. It is correct either way.

$$
\begin{array}{r}
13 \\
12 \\
\hline
26 \\
13 \\
\hline
156
\end{array}
$$

(partial product)
(partial product)
(total product)

*See p. 12 for explanation of asterisks.

Check for base seven:

Base 7		Base 10
13 =	$(1 \times 7) + 3 =$	$7 + 3 = 10$
12 =	$(1 \times 7) + 2 =$	$7 + 2 = 9$
$\overline{156} = (1 \times 7^2) + (5 \times 7) + 6 =$		$49 + 35 + 6 = \overline{90}$

The reason for this surprising result is that each individual step is true in either system. $2 \times 3 = 6$ whether the base is seven or ten. Similarly, $2 \times 1 = 2$, $1 \times 3 = 3$, $1 \times 1 = 1$, and $2 + 3 = 5$ in both systems. There is no carrying from one column to another, and so we need not consider how many of the units in one column are equivalent to one unit in the next column.

In either system, base seven or base ten, the explanation for indenting the "13," the second partial product, is the same. In both systems $13 = 10 + 3$ and $12 = 10 + 2$, so the example is

really		written more briefly as	
	$10 + 3$	"	13
	$10 + 2$	"	12
	$\overline{20 + 6}$	"	$\overline{26}$
$100 + 30$		"	13
$\overline{100 + 50 + 6}$		"	$\overline{156}$

Here is a harder multiplication example in base seven.

$$
\begin{array}{r}
65 \\
43 \\
\hline
261 \\
356 \\
\hline
4151
\end{array}
$$

Step 1: $3 \times 5 = 21$ (from Table 2). Write the "1" and carry "2." $3 \times 6 = 24$ and $24 + 2 = 26$, so we write "26" in front of the "1."

Step 2: $4 \times 5 = 26$. Write "6" in the sevens column and carry "2." $4 \times 6 = 33$ and $33 + 2 = 35$, so we write "35" in front of the "6."

Step 3: Add the partial products.

Check:

Base 7		Base 10
65 =	$(6 \times 7) + 5 =$	$42 + 5 = 47$
43 =	$(4 \times 7) + 3 =$	$28 + 3 = \underline{31}$
$\overline{4151} = (4 \times 7^3) + (1 \times 7^2) + (5 \times 7) + 1 =$		

$$1372 + 49 + 35 + 1 = 1457$$
$$\text{and } 47 \times 31 = 1457$$

Division is related to multiplication in the same way that subtraction is to addition. To divide 26_7 by 4_7, we must find what number multiplied by 4_7 gives 26_7. Table 2 shows us that $4 \times 5 = 26$, so $26 \div 4 = 5$.

Here is a long division:

$$\begin{array}{r} 32 \\ 25\overline{)1163} \\ 111 \\ \hline 53 \\ 53 \\ \hline \end{array}$$

Step 1: 2 into 11 might seem—from Table 2—to be 4, but $4 \times 25 = 136$, which is too big. $3 \times 25 = 111$.

Step 2: $116 - 111 = 5$. Bring down the "3."

Step 3: 2 into 5 is not given in Table 2. We see, however, that 2×3 is 6. But 6 is too big. Try 2×2 next. The number 4, being less than 5, allows us to use 2 in our answer. Thus 25 into $53 = 2$.

Check:

Base 7		Base 10
$1163 = (1 \times 7^3) + (1 \times 7^2) +$		
$(6 \times 7) + 3$	$= 343 + 49 + 42 + 3 = 437$	
$25 = (2 \times 7) + 5 =$	$14 + 5 = 19$	
$32 = (3 \times 7) + 2 =$	$21 + 2 = 23$	
and $437 \div 19 = 23$		

PROBLEMS

1. Use the tables on page 50 to do these computations. All the numerals are in base seven. Check in the decimal system.
   (a) $25 + 43$ (b) $251 - 63$ *(c) 32×154
   *(d) $434 \div 23$

2. What digits are needed in order to express any number as a numeral in the ternary system (base three)? Make the addition and multiplication tables for this system.

3. Count to ten in the ternary system. How can you determine if a number expressed in this system is odd or even?

*4. All the numerals in this problem are in the decimal system. Write each example in the ternary system, using the tables you just made.
   For instance, let's take $32 + 11$ (in base ten).

$$32 = (1 \times 27) + (0 \times 9) + (1 \times 3) + 2 = 1012_3$$
$$11 = \qquad\qquad (1 \times 9) + (0 \times 3) + 2 = 102_3$$

and

$$\begin{array}{l} 1012_3 \\ 102_3 \\ \hline 1121_3 \end{array}$$

Note: $2 + 2 = 4_{10} = 11_3$
$4_{10} = 4$ units $= 3$ units $+ 1$ unit
$\qquad = 1$ group of three $+ 1$
$\qquad = (1 \times 3) + 1$
$\qquad = 11_3$

Check:

$$1121_3 = (1 \times 27) + (1 \times 9) + (2 \times 3) + 1$$

or   =   27   +   9   +   6   + 1

or   =   43

and $32 + 11$ also equals 43.

(a) $15 + 29$ (b) $50 - 34$ (c) 9×14 (d) 7×25

(e) $80 \div 8$ (f) $119 \div 17$

ANSWERS AND EXPLANATIONS

1. (a) Base 7   Base 10

   $$\begin{array}{ll} 25 & = 14 + 5 = 19 \\ 43 & = 28 + 3 = 31 \\ \hline 101 & = 49 + 1 = \overline{50} \end{array}$$

   (b) Base 7   Base 10

   $$\begin{array}{ll} 251 & = 98 + 35 + 1 = 134 \\ 63 & = \phantom{98 + {}} 42 + 3 = 45 \\ \hline 155 & = 49 + 35 + 5 = \overline{89} \end{array}$$

   *(c) It is easier in any system to multiply two numbers if we take the smaller number as the multiplier.

   Base 7   Base 10

   $$\begin{array}{l} 154 = \\ 32 = \\ \hline 341 \\ 525 \\ \hline 5621 \\ = \end{array} \qquad \begin{array}{l} 49 \quad \oplus \quad 35 \quad + 4 = \quad 88 \\ 21 \qquad\qquad + 2 = \quad 23 \\ \hline \qquad\qquad\qquad\qquad\qquad 264 \\ \qquad\qquad\qquad\qquad\qquad 176 \\ \hline \end{array}$$

   $$5621 = (5 \times 343) + (6 \times 49) + (2 \times 7) + 1$$
   $$= \quad 1715 \quad + \quad 294 \quad + \quad 14 \quad + 1 = 2024$$

   *(d) Base 7   Base 10

   $$\begin{array}{r} 16 \\ 23 \overline{)434} \\ 23 \\ \hline 204 \\ 204 \\ \hline \end{array} \quad \begin{array}{l} 434_7 = (4 \times 49) + (3 \times 7) + 4 = \\ \qquad\qquad\qquad 196 + 21 + 4 = 221 \\ 23_7 = \qquad (2 \times 7) + 3 = \\ \qquad\qquad\qquad\qquad 14 + 3 = 17 \\ 16_7 = \qquad (1 \times 7) + 6 = \\ \qquad\qquad\qquad\qquad 7 + 6 = 13 \end{array}$$

   and $221 \div 17 = 13$

2. 0, 1, 2.

Addition

+	0	1	2
0	0	1	2
1	1	2	10
2	2	10	11

Multiplication

×	0	1	2
0	0	0	0
1	0	1	2
2	0	2	11

3. 1, 2, 10, 11, 12, 20, 21, 22, 100, 101. A number is odd if the sum of the digits is odd. A number is even if the sum of the digits is even. For example, let's take "12." The sum of 1 and 2 is three, which is odd. Therefore "12" is an odd number in the ternary system.

*4. (a) Base 10   Base 3

$$15 = 9 + 6 + 0 =$$
$$(1 \times 3^2) + (2 \times 3) + 0 = \quad 120$$
$$\underline{29} = 27 + 0 + 0 + 2 =$$
$$(1 \times 3^3) + (0 \times 3^2) + (0 \times 3) + 2 = \quad \underline{1002}$$
$$44 \qquad\qquad\qquad\qquad\qquad\qquad\qquad\qquad\qquad 1122$$

Check: $1122_3 = 27 + 9 + 6 + 2 = 44_{10}$

(b) Base 10   Base 3

$$50 = (1 \times 27) + (2 \times 9) + (1 \times 3) + 2 = \quad 1212$$
$$\underline{34} = (1 \times 27) + (0 \times 9) + (2 \times 3) + 1 = \quad \underline{1021}$$
$$16 \qquad\qquad\qquad\qquad\qquad\qquad\qquad\qquad\qquad 121$$

Check: $121_3 = (1 \times 9) + (2 \times 3) + 1$
$$= 9 + 6 + 1 = 16_{10}$$

(c) Base 10   Base 3

$$14 = (1 \times 9) + (1 \times 3) + 2 = \quad 112$$
$$\underline{9} = (1 \times 9) + (0 \times 3) + 0 = \quad \underline{100}$$
$$126 \qquad\qquad\qquad\qquad\qquad\qquad\qquad 11200$$

Check: $11200_3 = (1 \times 81) + (1 \times 27) + (2 \times 9)$
$$= 81 + 27 + 18 = 126_{10}$$

(d) Base 10   Base 3

$$25 = (2 \times 9) + (2 \times 3) + 1 = \quad 221$$
$$\underline{7} = \qquad\qquad (2 \times 3) + 1 = \quad \underline{21}$$
$$175 \qquad\qquad\qquad\qquad\qquad\qquad\qquad 221$$
$$\qquad\qquad\qquad\qquad\qquad\qquad\qquad\qquad \underline{1212}$$
$$\qquad\qquad\qquad\qquad\qquad\qquad\qquad\qquad 20111$$

Check: $20111_3 = (2 \times 81) + (0 \times 27)$
$$+ (1 \times 9) + (1 \times 3) + 1$$
$$= 162 \mid 9 \mid 3 \mid 1 = 175_{10}$$

(e) Base 10   Base 3

$$80 = (2 \times 27) + (2 \times 9) + (2 \times 3) + 2 = 2222$$
$$8 = \qquad\qquad\qquad\qquad\qquad (2 \times 3) + 2 = \quad 22$$

$$80 \div 8 = 10$$

$$\begin{array}{r} 101 \\ 22\overline{)2222} \\ 22 \\ \hline 22 \\ 22 \\ \hline \end{array}$$

Check: $101_3 = (1 \times 9) + 1 = 9 + 1 = 10_{10}$

(f) Base 10   Base 3

$$119 = 81 + 27 + 9 + 2 = 11102$$
$$17 = \qquad\qquad 9 + 6 + 2 = \quad 122$$

$$119 \div 17 = 7$$

$$\begin{array}{r} 21 \\ 122\overline{)11102} \\ 1021 \\ \hline 122 \\ 122 \\ \hline \end{array}$$

Check: $21_3 = 6 + 1 = 7$

The Binary System

The binary system (base two) is of special interest because it has only two symbols, 0 and 1. The addition and multiplication tables are very easy.

Addition

+	0	1
0	0	1
1	1	10

Multiplication

×	0	1
0	0	0
1	0	1

There are no more arithmetic combinations to learn than these. There are one hundred entries in each arithmetic table in the decimal system, from $0 + 0$ and 0×0 to $9 + 9$ and 9×9. If we have to learn up to 12×12, we have 169 entries in each table. What a wonderful relief it would be to our overtaxed brains if we had to learn only these tables with 4 entries—and such simple ones—in each. Even chimpanzees can do it.

On the other hand, it takes a large number of digits to write a moderately large number. We found before (see page 45) that $1727_{10} = 11,010,111,111_2$. This is rather discouraging and confusing to mere mortals, but a computer does not mind the length of a numeral. In fact, the binary system is made to order for computers, since the computer can use only two symbols. This is because a switch has two positions, on and off; a circuit can be in either of two states, with or without current flowing; a light can be either on or off. We can make each of these two conditions correspond to one of the two symbols and indicate all numbers in this way. With a row of four lights we can represent all numbers up to 15. The number 16 needs five lights in a row (see Problem 3, page 46).

If ▪ indicates a lighted bulb representing "1," and ▫ indicates an unlighted one representing "0," then

 stands for 1010_2 or $8 + 2$ or   10,
 stands for 111_2 or $4 + 2 + 1$ or   7,

and so on.

PROBLEMS

1. What numbers are represented by these arrangements of lights?

   (a) ▫▪▫▪   (c) ▪▫▫▫▫
   (b) ▪▪▫▫   (d) ▪▫▪▫▫

2. What is the largest number that can be represented (a) with five lights? (b) with six?

3. Write 6 and 7 in the binary system. Compute (a) $6 + 7$ and (b) 6×7 using these binary numerals. (Use the tables on page 57.)

*4. Write these binary fractions in the decimal system:

(a) $\dfrac{1}{10}$ (b) .1   (c) $\dfrac{1}{100}$ (d) .01   (e) $\dfrac{1}{11}$ (f) .11

ANSWERS AND EXPLANATIONS

1. (a) 101_2 or 5   (b) 1001_2 or 9   (c) 10000_2 or 16
   (d) 10101_2 or $21(16 + 4 + 1)$

2. (a) 11111_2 or 31
   (b) $111,111_2$ or $63(32 + 16 + 8 + 4 + 2 + 1)$

3. (a) $6 = 110_2$ (b) $7 = 111_2$
   $6 + 7$:

   110   *Step 1:* $0 + 1 = 1$.

   111   *Step 2:* $1 + 1 = 10$. Write the "0" and carry the "1."

   1101   *Step 3:* $1 + 1 = 10; 10 + 1 = 11$.

   Check: $1101_2 = 8 + 4 + 1 = 13_{10}$
   6×7:

110	or	111
111		110
110		1110
110		111
110		101010
101010		

   Check: $101010_2 = 32 + 8 + 2 = 42_{10}$

*4. (a) $\left(\dfrac{1}{10}\right)_2 = \dfrac{1}{2}$, since in the binary system, "10" means two.

(b) .1 is the same as $\dfrac{1}{10}$ in any system. $.1_2 = \dfrac{1}{2}$. We cannot call the "." a *decimal* point here. Maybe *binal* point would be an appropriate name.

(c) and (d) $\left(\dfrac{1}{100}\right)_2$ and $(.01)_2$ are both $\dfrac{1}{4}$. In any system,

$\dfrac{1}{100} = .01$

(e) $\left(\dfrac{1}{11}\right)_2 = \dfrac{1}{2+1} = \dfrac{1}{3}$

(f) $.11_2 = .1_2 + .01_2 = \dfrac{1}{2} + \dfrac{1}{4} = \dfrac{3}{4}$

How new is all this? Not very; it can be found in algebra texts from the 1880's. However, it used to be taught in advanced algebra courses. As supplementary material or as an additional topic called "Scales of Notation," it could be found near the back of the book.

As a subject for mathematicians, it is much older. The binary system was referred to in China some five thousand years ago. It was also a special favorite of the German philosopher and mathematician Leibniz (1646–1716). Representing God by "1" and nothingness by "0," he found great mystic significance in it, since everything could be created from these two ideas. "*Omnibus ex nihil ducendis sufficit unum.*" (One suffices to derive all out of nothing.) He thought this idea should serve to convert the Emperor of China from Buddhism to the worship of a god who created the universe from the void.

With such a venerable and respectable history, why should this be considered modern mathematics? The novelty is that now junior-high-school students learn it; it does not require scholars and mathematicians to understand it. Youngsters find it easy. Only adults, conditioned for years to the decimal system, think it is hard.

Chapter 5
Sets of Numbers and How They Behave

Here we extend the idea of number from the positive whole numbers, the simplest kind, to rational numbers, which include all the fractions. There are fundamental laws that govern mathematical operations. Axioms are the foundation of algebra and arithmetic as well as of geometry, and we use them to prove theorems in these areas also. All the manipulations of arithmetic and algebra follow logically from the axioms.

We have come this far in new mathematics without using the word *set*. Sets are in the air; school children learn "set theory." We are told that sets underlie all mathematics. It may be something of an anticlimax to discover that a *set* is nothing but a *collection*. It may be a collection of numbers, people, points, hats, or miscellaneous objects; the only requirement is that we must have some criterion for membership so that we can decide if a particular object belongs in the set or not.

A set is usually shown by listing its elements, writing them between braces, { }. The set of vowels in the English language is {a , e, i, o, u}. If there are too many to be listed, they can be described or otherwise indicated.

In this chapter we will consider only sets of numbers. Later we will talk about sets more generally.

A word of warning to the reader: You will have to get yourself in the proper frame of mind to read this chapter. As you start it, you may decide that you know all the substance of what is here and that it's just a matter of learning a few new words. If your aim is to do certain computations and solve a few equations, this is probably true. It is true, *if* you spent a fair amount of time and energy learning things like "Two minuses make a plus," "You put it on the other side of the equals and change the sign," "Invert the divisor," and so on. Sometimes, if you had a good teacher, all the rules made sense; sometimes, they seemed quite arbitrary. This is the sort of thing that evoked the comment that algebra was nothing but a bag of tricks.

Some years ago, before the advent of the new math, I had a student who couldn't seem to grasp the division of fractions. If the answer was $\frac{3}{4}$, Sue got $\frac{4}{3}$; if it was $\frac{a}{b}$, she got $\frac{b}{a}$. Her answer was always "upside-down"—numerator and denominator interchanged. Finally, we got to the bottom of her trouble, and she understood that she'd been inverting the wrong fraction. Her explanation: "Last year, we did it to the one by the window, and this year it's the one by the door."

This couldn't have happened if Sue had understood what she was doing, instead of following rules, not always correctly. The new approach is an attempt to minimize the number of rules and to get everything else to follow logically from them. Initially, it takes longer this way, and you may get impatient if you know how to get the answers by the old rules.

Therefore, you should try (for the time being at least) to ignore whatever algebra you painstakingly acquired and, as far as mathematics goes, try to be a junior-high-school student again. You know how to count, and you know the addition and multiplication tables, and that's all. We take it from there.

Natural Numbers and Counting Numbers

Our starting point is the set of natural numbers, $\{1, 2, 3, 4, \ldots\}$, where the row of dots means "and so on." We can picture them as points on a line.

THE NATURAL NUMBERS

Before men were sophisticated enough to wonder just what a number was, they had words and symbols for them, and spoke and wrote and used them. People could not get along without the natural numbers, so they were invented early in man's history. That many number words are similar in all Indo-European languages shows that these words are very old. They must have existed before the languages of today became separate tongues. For instance, the English "two" is "dva" in Sanskrit and Russian, "zwei" in German, "duo" in Latin and Greek, and "deux" in French. "Three" is "tri" in Russian and

Sanskrit, "treis" in Greek, "tres" in Latin, "trois" in French, and "drei" in German.

Having our set of natural numbers, what can we do with them? The first and most obvious thing is to use them for *counting*, but our set is not quite sufficient for this. We want these numbers to answer the question, "How many?" Of course, we can use them for such questions as "How many boys are there in Johnny's class?" "How many countries are there in the United Nations?" and so on. But what about "How many men have been to the moon?" Maybe in a few years there will be a number in the set to answer this question, but at present the answer is zero. So our set of counting numbers must contain one *element*, or *member*, that is not in the set of natural numbers.

$$1 \quad 2 \quad 3 \quad 4 \quad 5 \quad 6 \longrightarrow$$

THE NATURAL NUMBERS

$$0 \quad 1 \quad 2 \quad 3 \quad 4 \quad 5 \quad 6 \longrightarrow$$

THE COUNTING NUMBERS

The second use of our set of counting numbers (which is the union of zero and the natural numbers) is for *addition*. Let us look at the properties of this operation:

(1) Obviously, we can add any two numbers in our set and always get another number in the set. What is more, we never get two different answers from adding (correctly) the same pair of counting numbers. If Susie says, "6 + 7 = 13" and Johnny says, "6 + 7 = 15," at least one of them is wrong. The formal way of expressing these facts is to say that the set of counting numbers is *closed* to addition (that is, when we add numbers in the set we don't have to leave the set to get an answer) and that the sum (the result of addition) is *unique* (that is, there is not more than one answer). This is the *closure* axiom.

(2) It doesn't matter in which order we add two numbers.

$$\triangle + \square = \square + \triangle$$

What numbers make this statement true? Of course any pair will do.

$$5 + 2 = 2 + 5$$

Both are the same as both equal

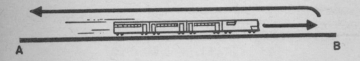

$a + b = b + a$. This property is known as the *commutative* law. It tells us that two numbers can be added in either order.

(3) There is an element in the set that can be added to any number without changing it.

$$a + \Box = a$$

This number is zero; it is called the *identity* element for addition.

(4) Addition is an operation connecting two numbers. Suppose we have three or more? What is meant by $3 + 8 + 6$? Of course, this must be computed in two steps, but what should the steps be? Should we say

$$3 + 8 = 11 \text{ and } 11 + 6 = 17$$

or

$$8 + 6 = 14 \text{ and } 3 + 14 = 17$$

Luckily, we got the same answer both ways. Or was it luck? It seems not. If we try with any other three numbers, the same happy result obtains. It does not matter how we group the numbers.

$$(a + b) + c = a + (b + c)$$

This is called the *associative* law. It tells us that in adding we can group numbers in any way we want.

"Which two of us should stick together first?"

"It doesn't matter; we'll all be together by the end. Associate with anyone you want to."

(5) Are there enough elements in our set of counting numbers to solve any equation involving addition? Not yet.

If $$17 + 21 = \square \quad \text{(new style)}$$

or $$17 + 21 = x \quad \text{(old style)}$$

then there is a number in the set to complete the equation correctly. The solution of this equation is the number 38, which is in our set. Similarly, the solution of

$$17 + x = 21$$

is the counting number 4. But what about

$$21 + x = 17$$

No number in our set will do. If we have no other numbers in our universe, then there is no solution. To remedy this unsatisfactory situation we must extend our universe and invent a larger set of numbers. Of course our counting numbers must be included in the new set.

The Integers* and the Axioms for Addition

The new elements in the set will be those numbers which when added to any natural number give zero as the sum. In modern language they are known as the "additive inverses" of the natural numbers. Traditionally, they are called "negative numbers." Thus, for any number, a, we create a new number, which we call

*An *integer* is a whole number.

"negative a" and write as "$-a$" such that $a + (-a) = 0$. The natural numbers are now called "positive." For example, since 4 was in the set of counting numbers, our expanded set contains -4, and by definition $4 + (-4) = 0$. The inverses of the negative numbers are already in the set. In other words, since $(-4) + 4 = 0$, 4 is the inverse, or negative, of -4 (because when it is added to -4 it gives zero). The inverse of zero, of course, is zero, since $0 + 0 = 0$.

In this new set of integers, the equation $21 + x = 17$ has a solution. Since $21 = 17 + 4$, we can write

$(17 + 4) + x = 17$

$17 + (4 + x) = 17$ (by the associative law)

$(4 + x) = 0$ (by the definition of zero as the identity element)

$x = -4$ (by our definition of additive inverses)

Of course, all these steps are not usually written out.

The number line now looks better; it had an incomplete look before. Now it goes on indefinitely in both directions. (On seeing

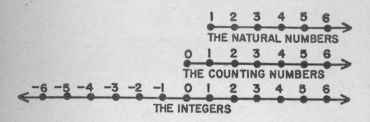

the number line with the counting numbers on it, an imaginative elementary-school child recently started talking about "left numbers" and how they behaved. He had invented negative numbers for himself.)

The associative law makes it easy to add integers without resorting to a lot of rules. For instance,

(1) $7 + (-3) = (4 + 3) + (-3)$
$= 4 + [3 + (-3)]$
$= 4 + 0$
$= 4$

(2) To add two negative numbers, such as -2 and -5, we note that

$$(-2 + 2) + (-5 + 5) = 0 + 0 = 0$$

But, by the commutative and associative laws,

$$(-2 + 2) + (-5 + 5) = (2 + 5) + [(-2) + (-5)]$$

Therefore, $0 = 7 + [(-2) + (-5)]$ and $[(-2) + (-5)]$ must be -7, since it is the number that must be added to 7 to get zero.

We will use this principle in the next example.

(3) $(-5) + 3 = [(-2) + (-3)] + 3$
$\qquad = (-2) + [(-3) + 3]$
$\qquad = -2 + 0$
$\qquad = -2$

With the extension of our set of counting numbers to include their negatives, we now have the set of all integers, positive, negative, and zero. The laws, or axioms, that describe their behavior with respect to addition are so fundamental that they are recapitulated here:

(1) For any two integers, a and b, there exists a unique integer, $a + b$, which is their sum. (Closure)

(2) For any two integers, a and b,
$\qquad a + b = b + a$ (Commutative law)

(3) For any three integers, a, b, and c,
$\qquad (a + b) + c = a + (b + c)$ (Associative law)

(4) There is an identity element, 0, such that, for any integer, a,
$\qquad a + 0 = 0$.

(5) For any integer, a, there is an integer, $-a$, its additive inverse, such that $a + (-a) = 0$.

There is certainly nothing novel or surprising about these observations. What is new is that we take explicit note of them and list them as axioms of our number system. Probably most of us met the word *axiom* first in geometry, where axioms used to be defined as "self-evident truths." We do not insist now that they be either obvious or true. We merely state that we shall use them as a basis for future work. Luckily, they are plausible enough so that no one is likely to object, but this is not the important point. We need axioms and definitions in arithmetic and algebra as well as in geometry, as they are essential for any deductive proof. Proof is part of all mathematics, and we use it not only in geometry but here and throughout all mathematics.

Notice that we have talked about negative numbers without ever mentioning subtraction. We define *subtracting a number* as being the same as "adding its inverse," and we already know how to add. Thus,

$$17 - 13 \text{ means } 17 + (-13) = 4$$
$$6 - 8 \text{ means } 6 + (-8) = -2$$
$$(-5) - (-11) \text{ means } -5 + (11) = 6$$

(since the additive inverse of -11 is 11).

$$(-10) - 4 \text{ means } -10 + (-4) = -14$$
$$12 - (-3) \text{ means } 12 + (3) = 15$$

(since the inverse of -3 is 3).

Problems

1. Is subtraction commutative? associative? *Prove your answers.

2. Which of the five laws on page 67 fit multiplication as well as addition?

Answers and Explanations

1. No to both.

$$a - b \text{ means } a + (-b)$$
$$b - a \text{ means } b + (-a)$$

and these are not the same; so subtraction is not commutative.

Or, since we can disprove a general statement by a single counterexample, we can try specific numbers.

$$7 - 5 = 2$$
$$5 - 7 = -2$$

and $2 \neq -2$, so subtraction is not commutative. (The sign $\neq$ means "does not equal.") Any pair of unequal numbers could be used. Similarly, subtraction is not associative, since

$$\left.\begin{array}{l}(8 - 5) - 1 = 3 - 1 = 2 \\ 8 - (5 - 1) = 8 - 4 = 4\end{array}\right\} \text{ and } 2 \neq 4$$

Or, more generally,

$$[a - b] - c = [a + (-b)] + (-c) = a + (-b) + (-c)$$
$$a - [b - c] = a + (-[b - c]) = a + (-b + c)$$
$$= a + (-b) + c$$

and these two results are unequal.

2. All five axioms hold, but the meanings of *identity element* and *inverse* are not the same. See the next sections.

The Axioms for Multiplication

If we consider a second operation, multiplication, with the set of integers, we can find many of the same properties as we found for addition.

(1) The product of any two integers is a unique integer.

(2) $a \times b = b \times a$. That is, four 3's are the same as three 4's. We are so used to this that possibly it is hard to see that it is not obvious. Why should these two addition problems yield the same answer?

$$
\begin{array}{cc}
3 & 4 \\
3 & 4 \\
3 & 4 \\
3 & - \\
\hline
\end{array}
$$

Thinking of products as areas is sometimes useful. Four columns with three dots apiece is the same as three rows with four dots in each.

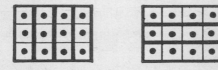

Thus the *commutative law* holds: $ab = ba$.

(3) What do we mean by $2 \times 3 \times 4$? Is it $(2 \times 3) \times 4$, or 6×4? Or $2 \times (3 \times 4)$, or 2×12? Again, as with addition, we get the same answer both ways. Therefore we may say $(ab)c = a(bc)$. This means that the *associative law* is true for multiplication.

(4) There is an *identity element* such that any integer multiplied by this element remains unchanged. The identity element in multiplication is *not* zero. The *multiplicative identity* is 1.

$$5 \times 1 = 5 \qquad 18 \times 1 = 18 \qquad a \times 1 = a$$

(Any integer multiplied by zero does change, as we shall see later.)

(5) *Multiplicative inverses* for most numbers do not exist in the set of integers. For example, the inverse of 2 should be the number which when multiplied by 2 gives 1, the identity for multiplication. This is $\frac{1}{2}$; no integer will work here. Let us abandon the notion of inverses temporarily.

We need *another* axiom to connect addition and multiplication. This one, called the *distributive law*, tells us that $a(b + c) = ab + ac$. We say that multiplication is distributive with respect to addition. For instance, $3(7 + 2)$ can be found in two ways. The first way:

$$3(9) \qquad \text{or} \qquad 27$$

The second:

$$(3 \times 7) + (3 \times 2) \qquad \text{or} \qquad 21 + 6, \text{ which is also 27.}$$

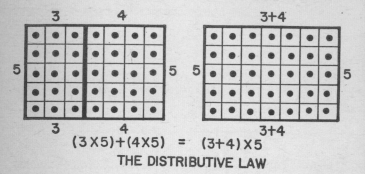

$$(3 \times 5) + (4 \times 5) = (3 + 4) \times 5$$

THE DISTRIBUTIVE LAW

We can use this law to show that the product of zero and any number is zero. Let us work out $a(a + 0)$ in two ways.

	$a(a + 0) = a(a)$	(since zero is the additive identity)
and	$a(a + 0) = a(a) + a(0)$	(by the distributive law)
Therefore,	$a(a) = a(a) + a(0)$	(since both equal $a(a + 0)$)
So,	$a(0) = 0$	(since zero is the additive identity)

The distributive law also enables us to prove the rules of signs for multiplication that were so troublesome in elementary algebra. We all learned that

$$3 \times 5 = 15 \text{ (no mystery here)}$$
$$3 \times (-5) = -15 \text{ (seems fairly reasonable)}$$
$$(-3) \times 5 = -15 \text{ (no worse than the preceding)}$$
$$(-3) \times (-5) = 15 \text{ (outrageous!—to most people at first sight)}$$

These results can be justified intuitively in many ways. For example:

If I save $5 a day ($+5$), in 3 days ($+3$) I will be $15 richer ($+15$) than I am now.

If I lose $5 a day ($-5$), in 3 days ($+3$) I will be $15 poorer ($-15$) than I am now.

If I save $5 a day ($+5$), 3 days ago ($-3$) I was $15 poorer ($-15$) than I am now.

If I lose $5 a day ($-5$), 3 days ago ($-3$) I was $15 richer ($+15$) than I am now.

This is hardly a proof, and it leaves many people with a dissatisfied feeling of having been pushed into agreeing with something they really don't accept. Maybe these proofs, using the distributive law, are more convincing.

Working out $5[3 + (-3)]$ in two ways, we get

$$5[3 + (-3)] = 5(0) = 0$$
and $\quad 5[3 + (-3)] = 5(3) + 5(-3) = 15 + 5(-3)$

Therefore, $15 + 5(-3) = 0$, so $5(-3)$ must be the same as -15.

More generally, working out $a[b + (-b)]$ in two ways,

$$a[b + (-b)] = a \times 0 = 0$$
and $\quad a[b + (-b)] = ab + a(-b)$

Therefore, $ab + a(-b) = 0$, so $a(-b) = -(ab)$, by the definition of additive inverse.

Similarly, working out $-5[3 + (-3)]$ in two ways,

$$-5[3 + (-3)] = -5 \times 0 = 0$$
and $\quad -5[3 + (-3)] = -5(3) + (-5)(-3)$
$$= -15 + (-5)(-3)$$

Therefore, $0 = -15 + (-5)(-3)$, so $(-5)(-3) = 15$. Moreover, in general,

$$(-a)(-b) = ab$$

The distributive law also accounts for the familiar rule about adding like terms. We used to say that $3a + 4a = 7a$ because 3 apples and 4 apples are 7 apples, but we couldn't work out $3a + 4b$ because we can't add 3 apples and 4 books. Unfortunately we got into difficulties in the next lesson when we had to multiply $3a$ and $4b$ and found it could be done—apples and books to the contrary notwithstanding. However, now, by the distributive law, $3a + 4a = (3 + 4)a = 7a$, but the distributive law cannot be applied to $3a + 4b$.

"Being a scientist is going to be a lot easier than I thought."

Drawing by Hoff; © 1958 The New Yorker Magazine, Inc.

PROBLEMS

Use the axioms to find an easy way of doing these computations: For example: $17(25) + 23(25)$, which by the distributive law,

$$= (17 + 23)25$$
$$= (40)(25)$$
$$= 1000$$

1. $16(19) + 16(31)$
2. $123(18) - 123(16)$
3. $151(-5) + 151(5)$
4. $37(28) + 63(28)$

ANSWERS AND EXPLANATIONS

Use the distributive law in each.

1. $16(19) + 16(31) = 16(19 + 31) = 16(50) = 800$
2. $123(18) - 123(16) = 123(18 - 16) = 123(2) = 246$
3. $151(-5) + 151(5) = 151(-5 + 5) = 151(0) = 0$
4. $37(28) + 63(28) = (37 + 63)28 = (100)28 = 2800$

The Rational Numbers

Back on page 70, we had to abandon the question of multiplicative inverses. For any number we would like to be able to produce another such that the product of the two is the multiplicative identity, 1. Only two numbers in the set of integers have inverses in that set. They are 1 and -1. For the others, we must extend our set as we did once before. The set of integers contains solutions for many equations involving multiplication:

$3 \times 5 = \boxed{?}$ 15 is in our set.

$3x = 18$ 6 is in our set.

$3x = 19$ No integral value of x can make this equation true.

We need a new set of numbers containing, if possible, all the integers and their multiplicative inverses. These inverses are usually called "reciprocals." The reciprocal of a is written "$\dfrac{1}{a}$"; and, by definition,

$$a \times \frac{1}{a} = 1$$

"It's happened, Alice — fractions."

All our previous axioms must still hold, and therefore all the theorems we proved for integers hold also. In particular (see page 70), for any number, a,

$$a \cdot 0 = 0$$

This means that there is no number which when multiplied by zero yields 1. Thus, zero has no multiplicative inverse and the symbol $\dfrac{\text{"1"}}{0}$ is meaningless; therefore, we can never divide by zero.

Since our set must be closed to addition, it must contain numbers like "$\dfrac{1}{3} + \dfrac{1}{3}$." By the distributive law,

$$\left(1 \times \frac{1}{3}\right) + \left(1 \times \frac{1}{3}\right) = (1 + 1)\frac{1}{3} = (2) \times \frac{1}{3}$$

Let us agree to write this as $\dfrac{2}{3}$.

*Using these definitions and our axioms, we should be able to derive the properties of fractions and the ways of computing with them without learning a lot of rules. Let's try some examples:

(1) $\dfrac{5}{7} - \dfrac{3}{7} = \left(5 \times \dfrac{1}{7}\right) - \left(3 \times \dfrac{1}{7}\right)$

$\qquad = (5 - 3)\left(\dfrac{1}{7}\right)$

$\qquad = 2 \times \dfrac{1}{7}$

$\qquad = \dfrac{2}{7}$

(2) Why is $\dfrac{10}{15} = \dfrac{2}{3}$? If we try multiplying each by 15,

$$15\left(\frac{10}{15}\right) = 15 \times \left(10 \times \frac{1}{15}\right) \qquad \left(\text{Definition of } \frac{10}{15}\right)$$

$$= 15 \times \left(\frac{1}{15} \times 10\right) \qquad \text{(Commutative Law)}$$

$$= \left(15 \times \frac{1}{15}\right) \times 10 \qquad \text{(Associative Law)}$$

$$= (1) \times 10 \qquad \left(\frac{1}{15} \text{ is the multiplicative inverse of } 15\right)$$

$$= 10 \qquad (1 \text{ is the multiplicative identity})$$

$$15 \times \frac{2}{3} = 15 \times \left(2 \times \frac{1}{3}\right) \qquad \left(\text{Definition of } \frac{2}{3}\right)$$

$$= (5 \times 3) \times \left(\frac{1}{3} \times 2\right) \qquad (\text{Commutative law})$$

$$= 5 \times \left(3 \times \frac{1}{3}\right) \times 2 \qquad (\text{Associative law})$$

$$= 5 \times 1 \times 2 \qquad \left(\frac{1}{3} \text{ is the multiplicative inverse of } 3\right)$$

$$= 10 \qquad (1 \text{ is the multiplicative identity})$$

Thus $\frac{10}{15}$ and $\frac{2}{3}$ are the same.

(3) Why is $\frac{a}{b}$ the reciprocal of $\frac{b}{a}$?

$$\frac{a}{b} = a \times \frac{1}{b} \qquad \text{and} \qquad \frac{b}{a} = b \times \frac{1}{a}$$

$$\frac{a}{b} \times \frac{b}{a} = \left(a \times \frac{1}{b}\right) \times \left(b \times \frac{1}{a}\right) = a \times \left(\frac{1}{b} \times b\right) \times \frac{1}{a}$$

$$= a \times 1 \times \frac{1}{a} = 1$$

Since $\frac{a}{b} \times \frac{b}{a} = 1$, each of these fractions is the reciprocal of the other.

(4) Show that $\frac{1}{3} \times \frac{1}{2} = \frac{1}{6}$.

$\frac{1}{6}$ is the reciprocal of 6. That is, $\frac{1}{6} \times 6 = 1$. Moreover, $\frac{1}{3} \times \frac{1}{2}$ is also the reciprocal of 6, since

$$\left(\frac{1}{3} \times \frac{1}{2}\right) \times 6 = \left(\frac{1}{3} \times \frac{1}{2}\right)(2 \times 3) = \frac{1}{3} \times \left(\frac{1}{2} \times 2\right) \times 3$$

$$= \frac{1}{3} \times 1 \times 3 = \frac{1}{3} \times 3 = 1.$$

Therefore, $\frac{1}{6}$ and $\frac{1}{2} \times \frac{1}{3}$ are the same. Similarly, in general,

$$\frac{1}{a} \times \frac{1}{b} = \frac{1}{ab}.$$

(5) Show that $\frac{a}{b} \times \frac{c}{d} = \frac{ac}{bd}.$

$$\frac{a}{b} \times \frac{c}{d} = \left(a \times \frac{1}{b}\right) \times \left(c \times \frac{1}{d}\right) = (ac)\left(\frac{1}{b} \times \frac{1}{d}\right)$$

$$= (ac) \times \frac{1}{bd} = \frac{ac}{bd}$$

(6) How can we add $\frac{2}{3}$ and $\frac{1}{4}$?

First note that we can't use the distributive law yet, as we did in the first example of this set. But, since $\frac{1}{4} \times 4 = 1$ and since $\frac{1}{3} \times 3 = 1$, we can write

$$\frac{2}{3} + \frac{1}{4} = \left[\left(2 \times \frac{1}{3}\right) \times \left(\frac{1}{4} \times 4\right)\right] + \left[\frac{1}{4} \times \left(\frac{1}{3} \times 3\right)\right]$$

$$= \left[2 \times \left(\frac{1}{3} \times \frac{1}{4}\right) \times 4\right] + \left[\left(\frac{1}{4} \times \frac{1}{3}\right) \times 3\right]$$

$$= \left[2 \times \frac{1}{12} \times 4\right] + \left[\frac{1}{12} \times 3\right]$$

$$= \left[8 \times \frac{1}{12}\right] + \left[3 \times \frac{1}{12}\right]$$

$$= (8 + 3) \times \frac{1}{12}$$

$$= 11 \times \frac{1}{12}$$

$$= \frac{11}{12}$$

By now we have done almost all the traditional sorts of examples with fractions without inventing any rules. We have added, subtracted, reduced, and multiplied them; only division is left. Let us define *division by any number* as meaning "multiplying by its reciprocal." (This is analogous to our definition of subtraction—adding the negative.)

Now $\frac{a}{b} \div \frac{c}{d}$ means $\frac{a}{b} \cdot \frac{d}{c}$ since $\frac{d}{c}$ is the reciprocal of $\frac{c}{d}$. (See Example 3 above.) All the arithmetic and algebra of fractions is now complete.

The set of numbers we now have consists of all the integers and all the fractions. These numbers are called *rational* numbers. A rational number is one that can be written as the *ratio* of two integers.

$\frac{1}{2}$ is rational; it is the ratio of 1 to 2.

3 is rational; it is the ratio of 3 to 1.

$-5\frac{1}{4}$ is rational; $-5\frac{1}{4} = \frac{-21}{4}$. It is the ratio of -21 to 4.

One important theorem that can be proved for this set is that, if the product of two numbers is zero, at least one of them must be zero. That is, if $ab = 0$, then either $a = 0$ or $b = 0$.

Proof:

If $a = 0$, our conclusion is true.

If $a \neq 0$, it has a reciprocal (multiplicative inverse), $\frac{1}{a}$.

Since $ab = 0$

multiplying each side by $\frac{1}{a}$,

$$\frac{1}{a} \times ab = \frac{1}{a} \times 0$$

$$\left(\frac{1}{a} \times a\right) \times b = 0$$

$$1 \times b = 0$$

$$b = 0$$

Therefore, either $a = 0$ or $b = 0$, which was what we wanted to prove. This result follows because there are multiplicative inverses, like $\frac{1}{a}$, in the set of rational numbers. In a set without them, this could not be proved.

PROBLEMS

1. Find an easy way of doing these computations. Which axioms are you using?

$$(a)\ (17 \times 60) \times \frac{1}{17}$$

$$(b)\ \left(\frac{3}{11} \times 15\right) + \left(\frac{3}{11} \times 7\right)$$

2. Is division commutative? associative? Why?

*3. Is division distributive with respect to subtraction? Why?

*4. Let the symbol ⬦ stand for "find the average of the numbers before and after this symbol." Thus, $8 ⬦ 14 = 11$, since $\frac{8 + 14}{2} = \frac{22}{2} = 11$. Is the operation ⬦ commutative? associative?

5. What is meant by "The additive identity has no multiplicative inverse"?

*6. What's wrong with this proof that $2 = 1$?

Suppose	$a = b$
Then, multiplying by a,	$a^2 = ab$
Adding $-b^2$	$a^2 - b^2 = ab - b^2$
or, since $-ab + ab = 0$,	$a^2 - ab + ab - b^2 = ab - b^2$
Using the distributive law,	$a(a - b) + b(a - b) = b(a - b)$
or	$(a + b)(a - b) = b(a - b)$
Multiplying by $\frac{1}{a - b}$,	$a + b = b$
Substituting a for b (since $a = b$),	$2a = a$
Multiplying by $\frac{1}{a}$,	$2 = 1$

ANSWERS AND EXPLANATIONS

1. (a) $(17 \times 60) \times \frac{1}{17} = (60 \times 17) \times \frac{1}{17}$ (Commutative law)

$$= 60 \times \left(17 \times \frac{1}{17}\right)\ \text{(Associative law)}$$

$$= 60 \times (1) \qquad \left(\frac{1}{17} \text{ is the multiplica-}\right.$$

$$\left. \text{tive inverse of } 17 \right)$$

$$= 60 \qquad (1 \text{ is the multiplica-}$$
$$\text{tive identity})$$

(b) $\frac{3}{11}(15) + \frac{3}{11}(7) = \frac{3}{11}(15 + 7)$ \qquad (Distributive law)

$$= \left(3 \times \frac{1}{11}\right)(11 \times 2) \left(\text{Definition of } \frac{3}{11}\right)$$

$$= 3 \times \left(\frac{1}{11} \times 11\right) \times 2 \quad (\text{Associative law})$$

$$= 3(1)(2) \qquad \left(\frac{1}{11} \text{ is the multipli-}\right.$$

$$\left. \text{cative inverse of } 11 \right)$$

$$= 6 \qquad (1 \text{ is the multiplica-}$$
$$\text{tive identity})$$

2. No to both. $\left.\begin{array}{l} x \div y = x \times \dfrac{1}{y} = \dfrac{x}{y} \\[2mm] y \div x = y \times \dfrac{1}{x} = \dfrac{y}{x} \end{array}\right\}$ These are not the same, so division is not commutative.

$\left.\begin{array}{l} (x \div y) \div z = \left(x \times \dfrac{1}{y}\right) \times \dfrac{1}{z} = \dfrac{x}{yz} \\[2mm] x \div (y \div z) = x \div \dfrac{y}{z} = x \times \dfrac{z}{y} = \dfrac{xz}{y} \end{array}\right\}$ These are not the same, so division is not associative.

*3. Is $(a - b) \div c = (a \div c) - (b \div c)$? Yes, since

$$(a - b) \times \frac{1}{c} = \left(a \times \frac{1}{c}\right) - \left(b \times \frac{1}{c}\right)$$

*4. $\diamondsuit$ is commutative, since

$$a \diamondsuit b = \frac{a + b}{2} \text{ and } b \diamondsuit a = \frac{b + a}{2}$$

Since $a + b = b + a$, these are equal. ⬦ is not associative. One numerical illustration can show this.

$$-(8 ⬦ 20) ⬦ 44 = 14 ⬦ 44 = 29$$
$$8 ⬦ (20 ⬦ 44) = 8 ⬦ 32 = 20$$

5. $\frac{1}{0}$ does not exist. In other words, we can't divide by zero.

*6. If $a = b$, then $a - b = 0$ and $\frac{1}{a - b}$ does not exist.

Now our number line, with all the rational numbers on it, looks quite different from the line with only the integers. It now seems

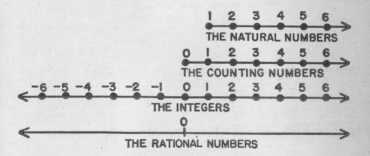

full. The rational numbers form a *dense set*, meaning that between any two rational numbers we can always locate another. The easiest way is to find the average of the two. Between $\frac{1}{4}$ and $\frac{1}{3}$, for instance, we can insert $\frac{7}{24}$ $\left(\frac{1}{4} + \frac{1}{3} = \frac{3}{12} + \frac{4}{12} = \frac{7}{12}\right.$; $\frac{1}{2}$ of $\frac{7}{12} = \frac{7}{24}\right)$. No two rational numbers are next to one another. There is no smallest positive rational number. Whatever very small one you think of, half of it is a smaller, positive rational number. However, looks are deceptive: We will soon find that this line full of points is also full of empty spots. In fact, the emptiness outweighs the fullness.

Solving Equations

By using axioms we should be able to solve simple equations without a lot of arbitrary rules. For instance:

$$3x + 5 = 26.$$

First step—old style: Move the 5 to the other side of the equal sign and change its sign from $+$ to $-$. This method of operating seems more like juggling than reasoning.

New style: Add -5 (the additive inverse of 5) to both sides. We can do this because we are told that $3x + 5$ and 26 are two ways of writing the same number. So, when we add -5 to this number, since sums are unique, we will get only one result. The result, however, may be written in two ways:

$$(3x + 5) + (-5) = 26 + (-5) \quad \text{or} \quad (21 + 5) + (-5)$$
$$3x + [5 + (-5)] = 21 + [5 + (-5)] \quad \text{(by the associative law)}$$
$$3x = 21$$

Second step: Multiply both sides of the equation by $\frac{1}{3}$, the multiplicative inverse of 3. $3x$ and 21 are two ways of writing the same number, and products are unique, so

$$\frac{1}{3}(3x) = \frac{1}{3}(21) \quad \text{or} \quad \frac{1}{3}(3 \times 7)$$
$$\left(\frac{1}{3} \times 3\right) \times x = \left(\frac{1}{3} \times 3\right) \times 7 \quad \text{(by the associative law)}$$
$$x = 7$$

After we understand the reasoning, of course it is unnecessary to write out all the details. Here is another example:

$$14n - 3 = 2n + 2$$
$$(12n + 2n) + (-3) = 2n + 2$$

Adding $-2n$ and 3 to both sides,

$$(12n + 2n) + (-3) + (-2n) + 3 = (2n + 2) + (-2n) + 3$$
$$12n + [2n + (-2n)] + (-3 + 3) = [2n + (-2n)] + (2 + 3)$$
$$12n = 5$$
$$\frac{1}{12}(12n) = \frac{1}{12}(5)$$
$$\left(\frac{1}{12} \times 12\right) \times n = \frac{5}{12}$$
$$n = \frac{5}{12}$$

Here are two theorems that help solve certain equations. The proofs depend on the existence of inverses.

(1) If $a + c = b + c$, then $a = b$.
(2) If $ac = bc$ and $c \neq 0$, then $a = b$.

In the proofs, we use the facts that the $=$ sign means that the quantities on either side are two names for the same thing, and that sums and products are unique.

Proofs

Theorem 1
$$a + c = b + c$$

Adding $-c$,
$$(a + c) + (-c) = (b + c) + (-c)$$
$$a + [c + (-c)] = b + [c + (-c)]$$
$$a + 0 = b + 0$$
$$a = b$$

Theorem 2
$$ac = bc$$

Multiplying by $\frac{1}{c}$,
$$ac \times \frac{1}{c} = bc \times \frac{1}{c}$$
$$a \times \left(c \times \frac{1}{c}\right) = b \times \left(c \times \frac{1}{c}\right)$$
$$a \times 1 = b \times 1$$
$$a = b$$

Note that in the second proof c cannot be zero. If it were zero, then $\frac{1}{c}$ would not exist. Zero has no multiplicative inverse. Since, by definition, division is multiplying by this inverse, we can never divide by zero.

Try making up some simple equations and solving them, new style. No problems are given here as you can use any of your own invention.

If your reaction to all of this is that of most people who already know some algebra, it is that the mountain has labored and brought forth a mouse. It is true that if your main objectives are to learn to manipulate positive and negative numbers, and to compute with fractions, and to solve equations, there are quicker ways: just memorize lots of rules. Here we have just the eleven axioms to learn (and since five are the same for multiplication and addition, there are really only six). All the algebra and arithmetic of the rational numbers is contained in them. Everything else grows logically from them. The process of understanding why $-(a + b) = -a - b$, for instance, is as important as the fact that they are equal, and nowadays we try to stress that process.

Of course, only at first do we write out with all the details every step in all these computations. After we are sure we understand why the procedures work, we write only as much as we need to in order to do the job. In this way, the final result should be that students of the new mathematics work with equal speed, at least equal accuracy, and much greater comprehension than students who learned the traditional way.

Chapter 6
Is Thursday Before or After Monday?

To show that there can be more than one arithmetic, we examine here some modular systems that have only a few numbers in them. They differ from ordinary arithmetic also in that the concepts of "larger" and "smaller" that seem so universal don't apply.

Clock-Face Arithmetic

Let us return to the integers.

$9 + 5 = 14$—or is it always? We know that 9 pencils and 5 pencils more always give a total of 14 pencils, but 5 hours after 9 o'clock is not 14 o'clock, except in the terminology used by the military services. In civilian life, 5 hours after 9 o'clock is 2 o'clock, so that $9 + 5 = 2$.

Similarly $3 - 8$ is usually -5, but $3 - 8 = 7$ when we find that time of day 8 hours earlier than 3 P.M.

The days of the week may be numbered from 1 to 7 as they appear in the columns of a calendar, with Sunday being 1; Monday, 2; and so on up to Saturday, which is numbered 7. Then $3 + 5 = 1$ or $5 + 3 = 1$, meaning that 5 days after Tuesday (numbered 3) or 3 days after Thursday (numbered 5) is Sunday (numbered 1). Also, $2 - 4 = 5$ in this system, since 4 days before Monday (2) is Thursday (5).

Using the months of the year, numbered similarly,

$$7 + (3 \times 5) = 10$$

that is, three 5-month periods after July (numbered 7) will bring us to October (10).

This sort of arithmetic is called *modular arithmetic*. If the smallest integer used is 1, then the *modulus* is the largest integer in the system. The *modulus* is also the number of integers needed. The clock and month examples both use 12 as the modulus. The days-of-the-week illustration uses 7.

Let us flex our mental muscles by examining this arithmetic.

If we want to use 5 as our modulus, we can imagine a clock face with only the numbers 0, 1, 2, 3, and 4 on it. We count by going around the dial. After 4 comes 5, which coincides with 0;

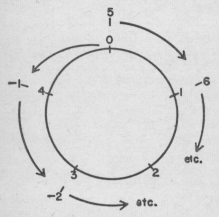

then comes 6, which falls at the same point as 1; and so on. Thus, in constructing a modular system, we map the whole infinite (or endless) set of integers (positive, negative, and zero) on a finite subset of them. Mapping all the integers on the set of integers from 0 to 4 will give us

$$
\text{zero and} \atop \text{positive} \atop \text{integers}
\begin{cases}
0 & 1 & 2 & 3 & 4 \\
5 & 6 & 7 & 8 & 9 \\
10 & 11 & 12 & 13 & 14, \text{ etc.} \\
\cdot & \cdot & \cdot & \cdot & \cdot \\
\cdot & \cdot & \cdot & \cdot & \cdot \\
\cdot & \cdot & \cdot & \cdot & \cdot \\
85 & 86 & 87 & 88 & 89, \text{ and so on.}
\end{cases}
$$

Or, going counterclockwise,

$$
\text{negative} \atop \text{integers}
\begin{cases}
-5 & -4 & -3 & -2 & -1 \\
-10 & -9 & -8 & -7 & -6, \text{ etc.} \\
-15 & -14 & -13 & -12 & -11 \\
\cdot & \cdot & \cdot & \cdot & \cdot \\
\cdot & \cdot & \cdot & \cdot & \cdot \\
\cdot & \cdot & \cdot & \cdot & \cdot \\
-55 & -54 & -53 & -52 & -51, \text{ and so on.}
\end{cases}
$$

The first column has all the multiples of 5. The second column, headed by "1," contains all numbers that have a remainder of 1 when divided by 5. Another way of describing the numbers contained in the second column is by saying that they are 1 more than any number that 5 goes into evenly. Still another way to say it is that they are 1 more than a multiple of 5. $86 \div 5 = 17$ with 1 left over, or $86 = 85 + 1 = (17 \times 5) + 1$
$$-54 = -55 + 1 = (-11 \times 5) + 1$$

Each of the numbers listed underneath "2" shares with 2 the property of being 2 more than a multiple of 5. (Note that -3 is 2 more than -5.) Each of the numbers in the column headed by "3" is 3 more than a multiple of 5. All the remaining columns (of both positive and negative integers) follow the same pattern of internal relationships.

Now, we treat all numbers in the same column as being equivalent. In the system with modulus 5, all the integers are partitioned into five sets and each integer belongs to exactly one of the sets. Any number in each set may be taken as a symbol for the whole set. This representative number is usually the smallest non-negative number.* Thus "3" now stands for any number in the set $\{ \ldots -12, -7, -2, 3, 8, 13, \ldots \}$. Using this convention and the five numerals 0, 1, 2, 3, 4, we can easily construct addition and multiplication tables with 5 as modulus. (These are familiarly referred to as the tables for "mod 5.")

Let's take the numbers 3 and 4. Although $3 + 4 = 7$, we write $3 + 4 = 2$ in our table, since 7 is represented in the set by "2" (7 being 2 more than a multiple of 5). The number 12, also, is in the same set. Thus, since $3 \times 4 = 12$, we write $3 \times 4 = 2$ in our table. We fill in the rest of the tables in the same way.

Mod 5 Addition					
+	0	1	2	3	4
0	0	1	2	3	4
1	1	2	3	4	0
2	2	3	4	0	1
3	3	4	0	1	2
4	4	0	1	2	3

Mod 5 Multiplication					
×	0	1	2	3	4
0	0	0	0	0	0
1	0	1	2	3	4
2	0	2	4	1	3
3	0	3	1	4	2
4	0	4	3	2	1

*There *is* a difference between "positive" and "non-negative" numbers. Zero is not a positive number, but it is not negative either. Therefore, non-negative numbers include zero. We might just as well have chosen the smallest positive rather than the smallest non-negative number to be the symbol for the set. In this case, our system would have contained "5" and not "0."

You should verify the entries in these tables.

Since subtraction can be thought of in terms of addition, and division in terms of multiplication, we can use the two tables for all four operations.

"$4 - 3 = ?$" means "What must be added to 3 to get 4?" Therefore, $4 - 3 = 1$.

"$2 - 3 = ?$" means "What must be added to 3 to get 2?" In ordinary numbers, $2 - 3 = -1$, since -1 must be added to 3 to get 2. We may write this also as $3 + (-1) = 2$. In the system with modulus 5, however, $2 - 3 = 4$. We look in the addition table at the row with "3" at the left and then across to the column headed by "4" to arrive at the result "2." Since $3 + 4 = 2$, then $2 - 3 = 4$ and $2 - 4 = 3$.

"$2 \div 4 = ?$" means "By what must 4 be multiplied to get 2?" Using the multiplication table, we find that $4 \times 3 = 2$, so $2 \div 4 = 3$. Also, $2 \div 3 = 4$. These results may seem strange. Perhaps you expect $2 \div 4$ and $2 \div 3$ to be fractions. They are *not*. It may help to remember that "2" represents any number in the set $\{ \ldots -8, -3, 2, 7, 12, \ldots \}$. Try $12(12 \div 4 = 3)$. Also, 2 is equivalent to -8; $-8 \div 4 = -2$, and -2 is one of the numbers represented by 3.

In this system we use only the symbols for five integers, each representing an infinite set of numbers which are equivalent. There are no fractions or negative numbers. However, their absence does not prevent us from having an arithmetic with the same axioms that apply to the infinite set of rational numbers. Let us verify this fact by checking with those axioms.

(1) *Closure for addition and multiplication.* This system is more obviously closed than any infinite set can be. The sum and the product of any two numbers are always 0, 1, 2, 3, or 4—all in the set.

(2) *The commutative laws.* If we check in both tables, we can see that these axioms hold. For instance,

$$2 + 4 = 1 \quad \text{and} \quad 4 + 2 = 1$$
$$2 \times 4 = 3 \quad \text{and} \quad 4 \times 2 = 3$$

Observing the symmetry of both tables around the diagonal from the upper-left to the lower-right corner is the simplest way to check this for all pairs of numbers.

(3) *The associative laws*. Let us test these with a sample for each.

$(1 + 3) + 1 = 4 + 4 = 3$ and $1 + (3 + 4) = 1 + 2 = 3$
$(2 \times 4) \times 3 = 3 \times 3 = 4$ and $2 \times (4 \times 3) = 2 \times 2 = 4$

For any numbers we try, we find these axioms hold.

(4) *The distributive law*. Let's check this by working out $4 \times (2 + 3)$ in two ways.

$$4 \times (2 + 3) = 4(0) = 0$$
$$4 \times (2 + 3) = (4 \times 2) + (4 \times 3) = 3 + 2 = 0$$

(5) *Identity elements*. Zero and 1 play their usual roles as the additive and multiplicative identities.

Zero added to any number leaves it unchanged.

1 multiplied by any number leaves it unchanged.

(As usual, the product of zero and any number is zero.)

(6) *Inverse elements*. The pairs 1 and 4, and 2 and 3 are additive inverses since $1 + 4 = 0$ and $2 + 3 = 0$. As always, zero is its own additive inverse since $0 + 0 = 0$. The number 4 is its *own* multiplicative inverse, since $4 \times 4 = 1$; whereas 2 and 3 are multiplicative inverses *of each other*, since $2 \times 3 = 1$. As always, 1 is its own multiplicative inverse, since $1 \times 1 = 1$. Zero, however, has no multiplicative inverse, since there is no number which when multiplied by zero gives 1.

By way of contrast, let us look at the system with 6 as modulus. For this, we use six symbols and divide all the integers into six sets. The multiples of 6 are represented by zero. Those integers that are 1 more than a multiple of 6 are represented by 1—and so on up to those that are 5 more than a multiple of 6 and that are represented by 5. Here are the addition and multiplication tables, made in the same way as before. For instance, $3 + 4 = 1$, since 7 and 1 are equivalent in this system. Also, $3 \times 4 = 0$, since 12 is a multiple of 6 and, so, is equivalent to zero.

Mod 6 Addition

+	0	1	2	3	4	5
0	0	1	2	3	4	5
1	1	2	3	4	5	0
2	2	3	4	5	0	1
3	3	4	5	0	1	2
4	4	5	0	1	2	3
5	5	0	1	2	3	4

Mod 6 Multiplication

×	0	1	2	3	4	5
0	0	0	0	0	0	0
1	0	1	2	3	4	5
2	0	2	4	0	2	4
3	0	3	0	3	0	3
4	0	4	2	0	4	2
5	0	5	4	3	2	1

There is nothing very startling in the addition table, but the multiplication table contains some surprises. Look at all the zeros in it. In our usual arithmetic and in the mod 5 system, we get zero as a product only if one or both factors is zero, but here both 3×2 and 3×4 are zero also. We proved earlier (page 78), using a multiplicative inverse, that if $ab = 0$, either $a = 0$ or $b = 0$. This statement is *not* true here. If we check all the axioms as we did for the mod 5 system, we find that all *except* the one about multiplicative inverses are true. We do have additive inverses though: $1 + 5 = 0$, $2 + 4 = 0$, $3 + 3 = 0$, and (as always) $0 + 0 = 0$. However, some numbers besides zero have no multiplicative inverses. Let's consider the numbers 2, 3, and 4. We cannot get 1 by multiplying any one of them by any number. Two or four times any number gives only zero, 2, or 4. Three times any number is always zero or 3. On the other hand, 5 and 1 are each their own inverses, since $5 \times 5 = 1$ and $1 \times 1 = 1$.

Since there are additive inverses, subtraction is always possible; but in the absence of multiplicative inverses, division is not. Just as we never can divide by zero since it has no multiplicative inverse, here in mod 6 we can't divide by zero, 2, 3, or 4. For example, "$3 \div 4$" means "find the number which, when multiplied by 4, gives 3"; here there is no such number.

If we have multiplicative inverses, if $ab = ac$ and if $a \neq 0$, then $b = c$. That is, we can divide both sides of an equation by the same number if that number is not zero. However, that is not true here. For instance,

$$3 \times 1 = 3 \times 5 \quad \text{(both are 3)}$$

but

$$1 \neq 5$$

It can be proved that we have multiplicative inverses whenever the modulus is a prime number. A prime number is an integer greater than 1 with no divisors except itself and 1. 5 is a prime number, but 6 is not, since it has divisors 2 and 3 as well as divisors 6 and 1. Thus a system with 7 or 2 as its modulus has multiplicative inverses and resembles the mod 5 system, since both 7 and 2 are prime. 2 is the only even prime number.

On the other hand, 10, 12, 14, 15, and so on are not prime numbers. A system with any non-prime number as its modulus resembles the mod 6 system. For instance, 15 is not prime as it has divisors 3 and 5. In the system with modulus 15, which uses symbols for the numbers from zero to 14, there exist numbers besides zero with no multiplicative inverses. Zero can be the product of two numbers even if neither is zero:

$$5 \times 6 = 0 \qquad 9 \times 10 = 0 \qquad 5 \times 12 = 0$$

We can't divide both sides of an equation by the same non-zero number. For instance,

$$5 \times 2 = 5 \times 8 \qquad \text{(both are 10)}$$

but

$$2 \neq 8$$

The simplest modular system is that with 2 as the modulus. Here are the tables.

+	0	1
0	0	1
1	1	0

×	0	1
0	0	0
1	0	1

In this system, all even numbers are represented by zero and all odd ones by 1. We may write these tables, therefore, in this fashion:

+	Even	Odd
Even	Even	Odd
Odd	Odd	Even

×	Even	Odd
Even	Even	Even
Odd	Even	Odd

They tell us the familiar facts that the sum of two odd or of two even numbers is even, and that the sum of an odd and an even number is odd. They also say that the product of two numbers is even if either or both is even, and is odd only if both are odd.

PROBLEMS

Use the tables on pages 87 and 89 to do these examples in the mod 5 and mod 6 systems, where possible.

For example:

$$3 \times (2 + 4) = 3 \times 1 = 3 \qquad \text{(mod 5)}$$
$$3 \times (2 + 4) = 3 \times 0 = 0 \qquad \text{(mod 6)}$$

1. $3 + 4$ 2. $3 - 4$ 3. 3×3 4. $1 \div 5$

5. $1 \div 3$ 6. $(4 \div 3) \times (3 \div 4)$

ANSWERS AND EXPLANATIONS

	Mod 5	Mod 6
1.	2	1
2.	4, since $4 + 4 = 3$.	5, since $4 + 5 = 3$.
3.	4	3

4. Impossible. There is no 5 in mod 5. Of course, 5 and 0 are equivalent, but $1 \div 0$ does not exist.

    5, since $5 \times 5 = 1$.

5. 2, since $3 \times 2 = 1$.

    Impossible. There is no number which when multiplied by 3 gives 1.

6. 1, since $4 \div 3$ is 3, $3 \div 4 = 2$, and $3 \times 2 = 1$.

    Impossible. Neither $4 \div 3$ nor $3 \div 4$ can be done.

Order

While the modular systems with a prime number as modulus obey all the axioms for rational numbers, they are nevertheless very different. The most obvious difference, of course, is that these are *finite*. The modulus 5 system has only five elements, and the system based on days of the week only seven. The set of rational numbers, however, is infinite.

Another important difference may be less obvious and that is the question of *order*. Since in mod 5, $4 + 2 = 1$, we must go 2 beyond 4 to reach 1. So we might conclude that $1 > 4$ ($>$ means "is greater than"). But $3 + 1 = 4$, so similar reasoning would tell us that $4 > 1$.

Of course we can't have it both ways. We have to abandon the idea of order in these clock-face arithmetics. This shouldn't be too surprising: after all, is Thursday before or after Monday?

For the set of rational numbers, order is no problem. If two numbers are not equal, one must be larger than the other. That is, either $a = b$, $a > b$, or $a < b$. ($<$ means "is less than." "$a < b$" and "$b > a$" mean the same thing.)

If $a > b$, then $a - b$ is a positive number, that is, a natural number or the ratio of two natural numbers. Also, if $a - b$ is positive, then $a > b$. This is our formal definition of $>$. Similarly, if $a < b$, then $a - b$ is negative, and vice versa. We can use these to prove some theorems about inequalities. For instance, let us show that

$$\text{if } a > b \text{ and } b > c, \text{ then } a > c$$

Proof:

"$a > b$" means "$a - b =$ some positive number"

"$b > c$" means "$b - c =$ some positive number"

Adding these, we find that $(a - b) + (b - c) =$ some positive number (since the set of positive numbers is closed to addition). Moreover, $(a - b) + (b - c) = a - c$. Therefore $a - c =$ some positive number. So, if $a - c$ is a positive number, then $a > c$.

Nowadays, we pay almost as much attention to inequalities as to equations. Basically, the same methods apply. Compare these solutions:

Equation	*Inequality*
$x - 7 = 5$	$x - 7 > 5$
$(x - 7) + 7 = 5 + 7$	$(x - 7) + 7 > 5 + 7$
$x = 12$	$x > 12$

In solving the equation, we use the fact that sums are unique. Both $x - 7$ and 5 are names for the same number. Therefore $(x - 7) + 7$ and $5 + 7$ are two ways of writing the same sum.

In solving the inequality, we need the definition of $>$. The sentence "$x - 7 > 5$" means that $(x - 7) - 5$ is a positive number. This is $x - 12$. Thus, since $x - 12$ is positive, $x > 12$.

Here is another pair:

Equation	*Inequality*
$5n = 35$	$5n > 35$
$\frac{1}{5}(5n) = \frac{1}{5}(35)$	$\frac{1}{5}(5n) > \frac{1}{5}(35)$
$n = 7$	$n > 7$

Here we use parts of the closure axiom in both cases. For the equation, it is the part about products being unique. For the inequality, we use the fact that $5n > 35$ means that $5n - 35$ is a positive number. Also, as the set of positive numbers is closed to multiplication, $\left(\frac{1}{5}\right)(5n - 35)$ is also positive. Therefore, $n - 7$

is positive, and $n > 7$. Notice that it was necessary here that $\frac{1}{5}$ the multiplier, be positive. Why? Because multiplying two positive numbers gives a positive result. However, if we have one positive and one negative number, the product is negative.

Compare this solution with the preceding one:

$$-5n > -35$$

Then

$$-5n - (-35)$$

or

$$-5n + 35 \quad \text{is positive}$$

However,

$$-\frac{1}{5}(-5n + 35)$$

or

$$n - 7 \quad \text{is negative}$$

Therefore

$$7 > n \quad \text{or} \quad n < 7$$

If we don't write out all the steps, but jump immediately from $-5n > -35$ to $n < 7$, we may be surprised at finding $<$ in the last line. (See Problem 1 below.)

PROBLEMS

*1. Notice that $7 > 3$ and that by multiplying by 2, we get $14 > 6$. But if we multiply by -2, we get $-14 < -6$, with the inequality sign reversed. Prove that this is generally true: (1) that if $a > b$ and c is positive, then $ac > bc$; and (2) that if $a > b$ and c is negative, then $ac < bc$.

2. Solve these inequalities and picture the solution sets on the number line. (The *solution set* is the set of all numbers that make the statement true.)

For example: $\frac{1}{2}x - 7 < 9$

add 7, $\frac{1}{2}x - 7 + 7 < 9 + 7$

or $\frac{1}{2}x < 16$

multiply by 2, $x < 32$

Thus, the picture of the solution set must show all numbers less than 32.

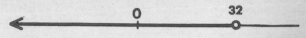

(a) $3x + 7 > 19$
(b) $15 - 2x \geq 23$ ($\geq$ means "is greater than or equal to.")
*(c) $x^2 > 25$
*(d) $x^2 \leq 4$ ($\leq$ means "is less than or equal to.")

ANSWERS AND EXPLANATIONS

*1. $a > b$, so $a - b$ is positive. If c is positive, then $(a - b) \times c$ is positive, since the set of positive numbers is closed to multiplication. $(a - b) \times c = ac - bc$, so $ac - bc$ is positive and $ac > bc$. If c is negative, $(a - b) \times c$ is negative since the product of a positive and a negative number is negative. Therefore, $ac - bc$ is negative, or $ac < bc$.

2. (a)
$$3x + 7 > 19$$
$$3x + 7 - 7 > 19 - 7$$
$$3x > 12$$
$$x > 4$$

(4 is not included. The empty circle at 4 indicates this.)

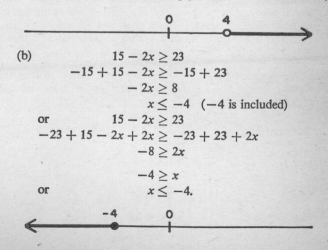

(b)
$$15 - 2x \geq 23$$
$$-15 + 15 - 2x \geq -15 + 23$$
$$- 2x \geq 8$$
$$x \leq -4 \quad (-4 \text{ is included})$$

or
$$15 - 2x \geq 23$$
$$-23 + 15 - 2x + 2x \geq -23 + 23 + 2x$$
$$-8 \geq 2x$$

$$-4 \geq x$$
or
$$x \leq -4.$$

*(c) $x^2 > 25$. If x is positive, it must be greater than 5.
If it is negative, it must be less than -5. For instance,
$(-6)^2 = 36$ and $36 > 25$.
Therefore, $x > 5$ or $x < -5$ is the solution set.

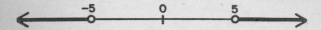

*(d) $x^2 \leq 4$. If x is positive, it is less than or equal to 2. If it is
negative, it is greater than or equal to -2. Therefore, it is
between -2 and 2 inclusive. The simplest way to write
this is

$$-2 \leq x \leq 2$$

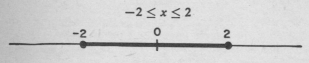

Chapter 7
Filling in the Holes

Here we look at further extensions of the number system, and go from the rational numbers to the real numbers and beyond. Real numbers are what people usually mean when they speak of "numbers."

Beyond the Rational Numbers

We mentioned before, near the end of Chapter 5, that the solid-looking line with all rational numbers pictured on it is really full of holes; in fact, the gaps outnumber the points. If we can imagine ourselves shooting point-sized bullets at the line at random, most of them would go right through without hitting any of the points representing rational numbers. This may be hard to believe since all the numbers we are likely to think of are rational. What other numbers are there?

Starting with the natural numbers and the counting numbers, we had to invent negative numbers in order to have a solution for the equation

$$21 + x = 17$$

or, in general, $x + a = b$ for any a and b, regardless of which is larger. Then we had to extend the set of integers by inventing fractions in order to solve the equation

$$3x = 19$$

or, in general, $ax = b$ for any a and b (excepting $a = 0$), whether or not b is a multiple of a. Now, let us consider the equation

$$x^2 = a$$

We can solve this in our set of rational numbers for some values of a, such as 25, 0, $\frac{9}{4}$, and any others which are perfect squares. But suppose that $a = 2$. What number when squared gives 2? No rational number will do, and we must extend our set of numbers once more if we want to have solutions to such equations. We write a solution to $x^2 = 2$ as $\sqrt{2}$. It is not new in mathematics that $\sqrt{2}$ is irrational. The ancient Greeks knew it, and it bothered them. It seemed to show something imperfect in the construction of the universe, as if the god who had charge of arithmetic had overlooked something. Here, in modern notation, is Euclid's proof that no rational number is equal to $\sqrt{2}$:

Suppose there were a rational number whose square is 2. Call it $\frac{p}{q}$ and be sure it is reduced to lowest terms. (If the numerator and denominator had any common factors, we could simplify the fraction by dividing them out.)

$$\frac{p}{q} = \sqrt{2}$$

Squaring both sides,

$$\frac{p^2}{q^2} = 2$$

Multiplying by q^2,

$$p^2 = 2q^2$$

Therefore, p^2 is even, since it is twice some number. Since the square of an even number is even, while the square of an odd number is odd, p itself must be even; call it $2r$. Now

$$(2r)^2 = 2q^2$$
or
$$4r^2 = 2q^2$$
$$2r^2 = q^2$$

By the same reasoning as before, q^2 is even, and therefore q is even. Now both p and q are even, so that q cannot be in lowest terms as we said it must be. Thus, this fraction cannot exist, and the $\sqrt{2}$ cannot be represented by any rational number.

In a similar fashion, we can show that $\sqrt{3}$, $\sqrt{5}$, $\sqrt[3]{2}$ (the cube root of 2, the solution to $x^3 = 2$), and other such roots are irrational. Other (and harder) methods are needed to show that there are many other sorts of irrational numbers. The number represented by the Greek letter pi (π), which is the ratio of the circumference of a circle to its diameter, is the most familiar. All these numbers, rational and irrational together, form the set of *real* numbers. There is a real number corresponding to every point on

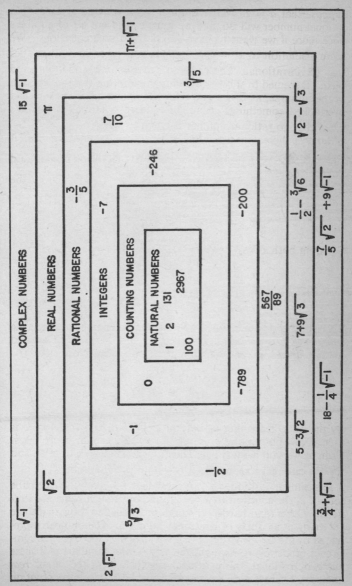

the number line and vice versa; the irrationals fill the gaps. For the real numbers, like the rationals, both the eleven axioms and the rules about order hold.

This is not the last extension possible. We need still other numbers to solve an equation like

$$x^2 = -1$$

so we invent $\sqrt{-1}$. This is not a real number since *any real number is positive, negative, or zero*. $0^2 = 0$; and positive and negative numbers, when squared, give a positive result. Thus, there is no real number whose square is -1 or any other negative number. Our new set, made up of $\sqrt{-1}$ and sums or products of this with the real numbers, is called the set of *complex numbers*. The real numbers are included in this set, and the eleven axioms hold here also. However, the complex numbers are not ordered. That is, we cannot say, for example, that

$$(1 + 3\sqrt{-1}) > 4\sqrt{-1}$$

or that

$$(1 + 3\sqrt{-1}) < 4\sqrt{-1}$$

since $(1 + 3\sqrt{-1}) - (4\sqrt{-1})$ is neither a positive nor a negative number.

See page 99 for a pictorial representation of our sets of numbers, with a few samples in each.

We will not discuss here complex numbers or any further extensions of the idea of number. When people talk of numbers, they usually mean the real numbers. Real numbers are those that are used to measure physical quantities like distance. It is easy to picture, for example, $\sqrt{2}$ inches. It is the diagonal of a square whose side measures 1 inch.

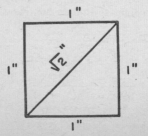

The real numbers include both *rational* and *irrational* numbers. Is there any way of telling them apart? Of course, by definition a number which can be written as a ratio is rational, so all fractions and mixed numbers are rational. What about decimals? A decimal like 2.47 is obviously rational, since $2.47 = 2\frac{47}{100}$ or $\frac{247}{100}$, which is a fraction. A decimal like .3333 ... (where the dots mean that the pattern continues forever) is rational, because we know it is a way of writing $\frac{1}{3}$. Suppose we didn't remember this; is there a way of showing it? If we let x stand for our decimal, .3333 ... , then

$$10x = 3.3333 \ldots$$

by subtracting

$$\frac{x = .3333 \ldots}{9x = 3.}$$

$$x = \frac{3}{9} \text{ or } \frac{1}{3}$$

Any decimal with a pattern that repeats forever can be shown to be a fraction. Here are a few other examples:

(1) If .83333 ... $= x$,

$$100x = 83.3333 \ldots$$
$$\frac{10x = 8.3333 \ldots}{90x = 75.}$$
$$x = \frac{75}{90} \text{ or } \frac{5}{6}$$

Notice that the pattern does not have to begin at the beginning of the decimal. Here it began with the second digit, but it could begin any place so long as it then continues forever.

(2) If .123123123 ... is x,

$$1000x = 123.123123 \ldots$$
$$\frac{x = .123123 \ldots}{999x = 123.}$$
$$x = \frac{123}{999} \text{ or } \frac{41}{333}$$

(3) If .249999 ... is x,

$$1000x = 249.999\ldots$$
$$100x = 24.999\ldots$$
$$900x = 225.$$
$$x = \frac{225}{900} \text{ or } \frac{1}{4}$$

We might have foreseen this, since .24999 ... gets closer and closer to .25, which is $\frac{1}{4}$.

If we try going in the other direction, we can see that any fraction can be written as a decimal which either terminates (comes out even), like .75, .298, etc., or which goes on forever in some repeating pattern. For example, $\frac{6}{11}$ (by division) is .545454 ... A more complicated one is $\frac{2}{13}$. Here is the division:

```
        .15384615 ...
  13)2.00000000
     13
     ──
      70
      65
      ──
       50
       39
       ──
       110
       104
       ───
         60
         52
         ──
          80
          78
          ──
          20
          13
          ──
           70
```

Thus, $\frac{2}{13} = .153846153846\ldots$ Note the italicized numbers in the long division. These remainders can only be numbers from 1 to 12 inclusive. Thus, after twelve steps, at most, we must get one of them for the second time. Actually it took only six steps. When this happens, the computation must proceed as it did from the beginning, and the pattern must continue repeating from there on.

Any fraction can be written as a terminating or a repeating decimal. Any such decimal is a rational number. Irrational numbers, written as decimals, never terminate or show a pattern that repeats a digit or group of digits indefinitely.

PROBLEMS

1. Show that 1.41 is rational and is smaller than $\sqrt{2}$. Show that 1.42 is rational and is larger than $\sqrt{2}$.

2. Show that $\dfrac{140}{99}$ is between 1.41 and 1.42. Determine if it is larger than, equal to, or smaller than $\sqrt{2}$.

3. $3\frac{1}{7}$, 3.14, and 3.1416 are often used for π. Are they all equal? Are any or all of them equal to π?

4. Show that .252525 . . . , where the row of dots means that the pattern continues indefinitely, is a rational number. (Hint: Let x = this number and consider $100x$.)

ANSWERS AND EXPLANATIONS

1. $1.41 = 1\dfrac{41}{100}$ or $\dfrac{141}{100}$. Thus it is the ratio of two integers and so rational.

   $1.41^2 = 1.9881$. Therefore, $1.41 < \sqrt{2}$.

   $1.42 = \dfrac{142}{100}$ or $\dfrac{71}{50}$

   $1.42^2 = 2.0164$. Therefore, $1.42 > \sqrt{2}$.

2. By long division, $\dfrac{140}{99} = 1.414141 \ldots$ which is larger than 1.41 and smaller than 1.42.

   $\left(\dfrac{140}{99}\right)^2 = \dfrac{19600}{9801}$. This is less than $\dfrac{19602}{9801}$ which is equal to 2.

   Therefore, $\dfrac{140}{99} < \sqrt{2}$ (but it is quite close).

3. To four decimal places, $3\frac{1}{7} = 3.1429$

   $3.14 = 3.1400$

   3.1416 is between these.

All are unequal, and none is exactly equal to π. No rational number is.

4.
$$100x = 25.2525 \ldots$$
$$x = .2525 \ldots$$
$$\overline{99x = 25}$$

Subtracting,

$$x = \frac{25}{99}, \text{ which is rational.}$$

How Many Is Infinite?

If any idea about modern mathematics has emerged so far, it should be that we are interested in proving our assertions. We have proved even things that may seem obvious. The proof is often stressed more than the fact. Certainly we should not let pass unchallenged and unproved the very *un*obvious statement that there are more holes than points in the rational number line, more irrationals than rationals. To prove this, we must take a rather long detour.

Of course, there are an infinite number of natural numbers, of integers, of rationals, and of reals. Until the end of the nineteenth century, that was the whole story. When you knew that a certain number was larger than any natural number, you knew all there was to be known about its size. The number of grains of sand in all the beaches of the world, the number of drops of water in all the oceans, the number of atoms in all the continents are all very large numbers, but they are not infinite. They are finite and countable, although it might take centuries to count them. Archimedes estimated that the number of grains of sand it would take to fill the universe is (in modern notation) around 10^{63}—an enormous, unimaginable number—but still finite. There are larger numbers, 10^{64} for instance; we will never run out of numbers. *Infinity* is larger than any such number. There are an infinite number of integers. Are there more rational or real numbers than there are integers?

Georg Cantor (1845–1918) developed the theory of infinite sets, so as to be able to answer such questions.

It may help to start by wondering how we compare the sizes of any numbers. If we want to know whether Joe or John has more marbles, we can count them. But if Joe and John are too young to be able to count, they can still find out who has more. They can pair off their marbles, one of Joe's to one of John's. When all of Joe's are paired off, if John still has some left unpaired, of course they know that John has more. We can easily see whether there are more people or seats in a theatre—without counting. If everyone is seated and there are still empty seats, there are more seats. If every seat is taken and there are standees, there are more people.

For infinite sets, of course, counting is impossible. We can compare them only by trying to pair off the elements. We call this "putting the sets into one-to-one correspondence." If this can be done, they have the same number of elements. Some strange results follow from this method of comparison.

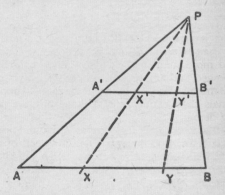

There are as many points on the 1″-line segment $A'B'$ as on the 2″-segment AB. For every point such as X on AB we can find a point X' on $A'B'$. For every point like Y' on $A'B'$ we can find a point Y on AB. By drawing lines through P as shown, we can pair off the points on the two segments and never run out of points on either. Therefore, they have the same number of points.

What's more, there is the same number of points on the semi-circular arc AB (not counting A and B) as on the whole infinite

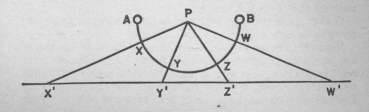

line. The same reasoning applies here. For any point such as X on the arc, we can find a point X' on the line by drawing PX and extending it until it hits the line. For any point as Y' on the line, PY' intersects the arc at a corresponding point Y. Therefore, we shall never run out of points on either. We have a one-to-one correspondence between the points on the arc and the points on the line. The number of points on one is thus the same as the number of points on the other.

There is the same number of positive, even numbers as of natural numbers, since we can pair the two sets off this way:

$$
\begin{array}{ccccccc}
1 & 2 & 3 & 4 & 5 & 6 & 7 \ldots \\
\updownarrow & \updownarrow & \updownarrow & \updownarrow & \updownarrow & \updownarrow & \updownarrow \\
2 & 4 & 6 & 8 & 10 & 12 & 14 \ldots
\end{array}
$$

We won't run out of one set before the other.

The set of natural numbers and any set that can be put into one-to-one correspondence with it are called *denumerable* or *enumerable*. Thus, the natural numbers and the positive, even numbers are *denumerably infinite*.

What about all integers? This set is also denumerable since we can arrange the integers in a list that will contain all of them:

corresponding to
$$
\begin{array}{ccccccc}
0 & 1 & -1 & 2 & -2 & 3 & -3 \ldots \\
\updownarrow & \updownarrow & \updownarrow & \updownarrow & \updownarrow & \updownarrow & \updownarrow \\
1 & 2 & 3 & 4 & 5 & 6 & 7 \ldots
\end{array}
$$

All perfect squares can also be put into one-to-one correspondence with the natural numbers:

$$
\begin{array}{ccccc}
1 & 4 & 9 & 16 & 25 \ldots \\
\updownarrow & \updownarrow & \updownarrow & \updownarrow & \updownarrow \\
1 & 2 & 3 & 4 & 5 \ldots
\end{array}
$$

There are many such sets. For instance,

$$1 \quad 8 \quad 27 \quad 64 \quad \ldots \quad \text{(all perfect cubes)}$$

$$2 \quad 4 \quad 8 \quad 16 \quad \ldots \quad \text{(all powers of 2)}$$

and others can also be put into one-to-one correspondence with the natural numbers.

One characteristic of an infinite set—very unlike anything with a finite set—is that a part of it can contain the same number of elements as the whole, even though there may be an infinite number of elements in the whole missing in the part.

Sets that can be put into one-to-one correspondence with each other are said to be *equivalent*. All sets equivalent to the natural numbers are denumerable.

Sometimes it takes some ingenuity to find a way of arranging the elements of a set so as to be able to pair them off with the natural numbers. They cannot always be arranged in order of size; the integers, for example, were not. Although intuitively we may feel that there are lots more rational numbers than integers, these also are denumerable. Suppose we arrange them by taking first those whose numerators and denominators add up to 1, then those in which they add up to 2, then 3, and so on. Within each group we will arrange them in order of the size of the numerators. Any duplicates we will delete. We will use only positive numerators and denominators.

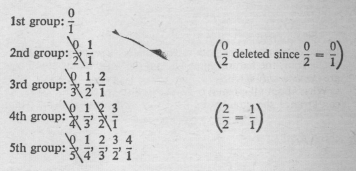

1st group: $\dfrac{0}{1}$

2nd group: $\dfrac{0}{2}\ \dfrac{1}{1}$ $\left(\dfrac{0}{2} \text{ deleted since } \dfrac{0}{2} = \dfrac{0}{1}\right)$

3rd group: $\dfrac{0}{3}\ \dfrac{1}{2},\ \dfrac{2}{1}$

4th group: $\dfrac{0}{4}\ \dfrac{1}{3},\ \dfrac{2}{2}\ \dfrac{3}{1}$ $\left(\dfrac{2}{2} = \dfrac{1}{1}\right)$

5th group: $\dfrac{0}{5}\ \dfrac{1}{4},\ \dfrac{2}{3},\ \dfrac{3}{2}\ \dfrac{4}{1}$

And so on.
The final arrangement, now alternating positive and negative numbers, is

$$0 \quad 1 \quad -1 \quad \tfrac{1}{2} \quad -\tfrac{1}{2} \quad 2 \quad -2 \quad \tfrac{1}{3} \quad -\tfrac{1}{3} \quad 3 \quad -3 \quad \tfrac{1}{4} \quad -\tfrac{1}{4} \quad \tfrac{2}{3} \ \ldots;$$
$$\updownarrow \quad \updownarrow \quad \updownarrow \quad \updownarrow \quad \updownarrow \quad \updownarrow \quad \updownarrow \quad \updownarrow \quad \updownarrow \quad \updownarrow \quad \updownarrow \quad \updownarrow \quad \updownarrow \quad \updownarrow$$
$$1 \quad 2 \quad 3 \quad 4 \quad 5 \quad 6 \quad 7 \quad 8 \quad 9 \quad 10 \quad 11 \quad 12 \quad 13 \quad 14 \ \ldots;$$

Thus, the rational numbers can be made to correspond to the natural numbers. Each rational number will eventually appear in this listing, so this set is also denumerable.

By now it must seem as if all infinite sets are denumerable. Not so! Let us look at the set of real numbers. It would not be enough for us to have tried to arrange all of them in some list, one after another, and to have failed. This could mean merely that we weren't ingenious enough and that someone cleverer might succeed. What we must do is to show that no scheme could possibly work—that whatever listing anyone devises cannot contain all real numbers. So let's let George do it, and then look at his result. We ask him to list only his set of reals between zero and 1 in such a way that there is a first, second, third, and so on, so that they can be paired off with the natural numbers. If he thinks the whole set is denumerable, this limited set must be likewise. He claims all real numbers between zero and 1 appear in his list. All his numbers can be written as infinite decimals. If they terminate, as does .25, we can write them as infinite decimals in either of two ways: .25 = .2500000 ... or .2499999 ... (see Example 3, page 102). Let us agree on either one of these forms and use it throughout. Now George's list may look like this:

.827556842 ...   corresponding to 1
.063191919 ...   corresponding to 2
.529782137 ...   corresponding to 3
.329565029 ...   corresponding to 4

and so on. We don't need to know how he constructed the list. We merely show that we can find at least one real number between zero and 1 not in his list, no matter how he did it. Note that the numbers on his list are not arranged in order of size. All of them have a denumerably infinite number of digits, and there are a denumerably infinite number of them. Some of them must show a pattern that repeats forever from some point on; these are the rational numbers. The others are irrational. George asserts that all the real numbers between zero and 1 appear here somewhere. If we were to choose a real number at random, we couldn't show that it is not on his list merely by looking and failing to find it. We could never inspect his whole list since it is infinitely long. We must construct our number very carefully in order to be sure it is not somewhere on his list. Since George's first number begins with "8," our number will have for its first digit any number except "8," say "5." Then, however we go on, it will not be George's first number. The second digit will not be "6." Suppose we use "4"; then it won't be his second number. The third digit will not be "9," to make it differ from his third number. The fourth digit will not be "5," so it won't be his fourth number, and so on for all the infinite number of digits and numbers.

Our number .5481 . . . cannot be in George's list at all, no matter how he made his list, since we are sure it differs from each of his numbers in at least one digit. For instance, do you think our number might be the 369th in his list? No, because it differs in at least the 369th digit. This shows that *all* real numbers are not in this list (since we found one that is not), however this list was made. Thus, there can be no listing of all reals, they cannot be put into one-to-one correspondence with the natural numbers, and they are not denumerable. As infinite as are the natural numbers, integers, and rationals, there are more reals, infinitely more.

If we unite two denumerable sets, the resulting set is still denumerable. We can show this by taking elements alternately from the two sets, as we did with the positive and negative integers when we showed that all the integers are denumerable. Therefore, if the rationals and irrationals together form a non-denumerable set, while the rationals alone are denumerable, the irrationals can't be denumerable. There are more numbers in the set of irrational numbers than in any of the denumerable sets we mentioned. Therefore, there are more irrationals than rationals, and, in the rational-number line, the gaps do outnumber the points.

PROBLEMS

1. Show that the set of all even integers (positive, negative, and zero) is denumerable.

*2. Use this diagram to show that the rationals are denumerable.

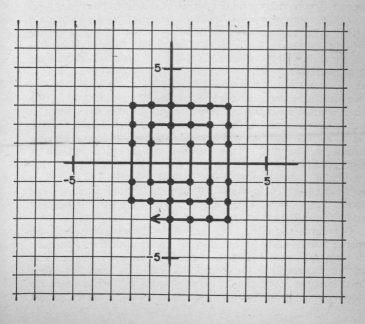

ANSWERS AND EXPLANATIONS

1. 0   2   −2   4   −4   6   −6   ...
    ↕   ↕   ↕   ↕   ↕   ↕   ↕
    1   2   3   4   5   6   7   ...

*2. Follow the spiral line, and at each point form the number that is the ratio of its distance from the vertical line to its distance from the horizontal line. All points on the horizontal line must be omitted, since the ratio of any number to zero is meaningless. Any numbers we find we have already listed, we will delete.

Our listing now is

$$1 \quad -1 \quad 0 \quad -\frac{1}{2} \quad \frac{1}{2} \quad 2 \quad -2 \quad -\frac{2}{3} \quad -\frac{1}{3} \quad \frac{1}{3} \quad \frac{2}{3} \quad \frac{3}{2} \quad 3 \quad -3$$

    ↕   ↕   ↕   ↕   ↕   ↕   ↕   ↕   ↕   ↕   ↕   ↕   ↕   ↕
    1   2   3   4   5   6   7   8   9   10 11 12 13 14

All points with integral distances from the lines will eventually be on the spiral, so all rational numbers will eventually be in the list.

The real numbers correspond to the points on a line. For every real number there is a point at that distance from the zero point, and for every point, there is a real number representing its distance. Thus, the points on a line (or on a line segment, see pages 105 and 106) form a non-denumerable set.

Cantor, who studied these infinite sets, called the numbers of elements in such sets *transfinite* numbers. We have met two of them: (1) the number of elements in a denumerable set and (2) the number of points on a line. There are many others—in fact, an infinite number of transfinite numbers—but we shall go no further.

An unanswered, and maybe unanswerable, question is, "Are there any transfinite numbers greater than the first of these and smaller than the second?" What do you think?

Analytic Geometry

Analytic geometry is a fancy name for pictorial thinking, thinking about numbers and relations between them by visualizing them as graphs. Graphs are now commonplace. Every newspaper prints graphs showing soaring taxes, plunging stock prices, rising and falling levels of production, and so on. What's more, most newspaper readers understand what they mean. As recently as the early 1900's, this would not have been true; even many well-educated people were untrained in the art of reading graphs. One of H. G. Wells' (1866–1947) projects for civilizing society included teaching this skill, and his urging has had effect.

Analytic geometry used to be entirely a college course, and in its more formal and advanced aspects, it still is. However, it has crept down into the high-school and junior-high-school curricula, and simple work with graphs is being introduced into some elementary-school courses.

The basic idea is not obvious. It took mathematical thinkers a couple of thousand years to hit on it. However, once you think of it, it's very easy, especially for people who live in a planned city with numbered streets and avenues. A location in such a city is pinpointed by a pair of numbers. For instance, the address *"720 6th Avenue"* will tell anyone who knows the city in question how to get to that address.

If points are described by pairs of numbers, it is natural to look for the answers to two questions: If the points form some pattern, what is the relation between the two numbers in the pair? If the two numbers are always related in a particular way by some special equation or statement of inequality, what effect will this have on the arrangements of the points they locate?

Analytic geometry discusses the answers to these questions. It is a sort of hybrid between algebra and geometry, since it deals with lines and points, usually classified as geometric concepts, and with equations and inequalities, which are traditionally algebraic. It is therefore appropriate to include work with graphs in both algebra and geometry courses, and this is now being done. Many proofs and problems in geometry can be done more easily by applying algebraic techniques, describing the points and lines of a diagram by the number-pairs and equations that represent them. On the other hand, having a geometric representation of an algebraic relationship often makes it more concrete and more meaningful. Through analytic geometry, algebra and geometry come together, and each illuminates the other.

Instead of reserving this marriage between two main branches of mathematics for later courses after students have already studied them separately, we now introduce it sooner, so that it can be more fruitful and useful in early work.

Chapter 8

From the Number Line to the Number Plane

A pair of numbers can be used to locate a point on a plane. The two numbers of the pair may be connected by an equation or an inequality. The set of all points described by such pairs is the graph of the relation. The concept of a "function" is an important one, and we examine many sorts of functions. Solution sets of equations and of inequalities can be shown on the Cartesian plane. An interesting and useful application of sets of simultaneous inequalities is in *linear programming*.

So far, we have been discussing single numbers and looking at their graphs on the number line. With numbers as with people, pairs are usually more interesting. There is often more to be said about the relationship between the two than about either one alone. In any pair, it makes considerable difference which is which: if we are talking about boy-girl pairs and mentioning the boys first, then the pair Leslie and Robin is surely not the same as the pair Robin and Leslie. So our pairs will be *ordered* pairs. Consequently we shall learn to recognize that (3, 4) is not the same as (4, 3).

We have already used the conventional way of graphing or picturing ordered pairs (see Problem 2, page 109). We need two *number lines* at right angles, a horizontal one called the *x*-axis, and a vertical one called the *y*-axis. An ordered pair describes a point: the first number tells how far left or right the point is from the *y*-axis, and the second tells how far the point is above or below the *x*-axis.

René Descartes (1596–1658) first explored in detail this method of representing numbers and the relations between them graphically. The number plane is therefore called the *Cartesian plane*.

113

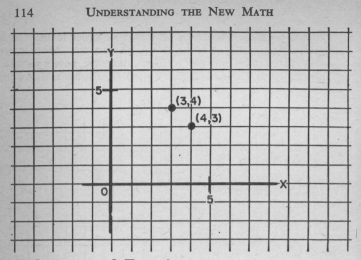

Relations and Functions

A *relation*, then, is "a set of ordered pairs." It could look something like this:

$$\{(3, 4), (7, -2), (-4, 0), (1, -3), (3, 1)\}$$

The first number in each pair is the *x*-value and the second the *y*-value of a point on the graph. The graph of this relation is:

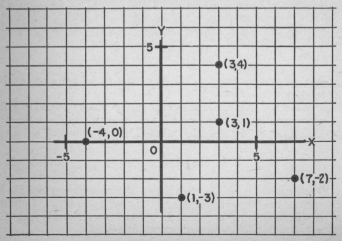

There is no particular rhyme or reason or order in the graph above, as the relation is an arbitrary, planless one. More interesting graphs of ordered-pair relations, of course, have a pattern. This set, $\{(0, 5), (1, 4), (2, 3), (3, 2), (4, 1), (5, 0)\}$, has as its graph:

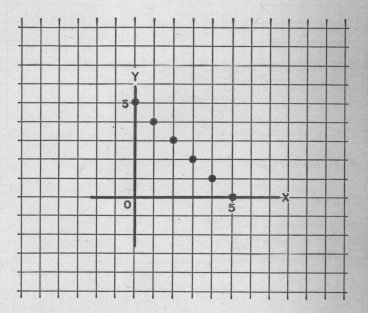

The pattern is obvious. This is the set of all pairs of positive integers whose sum is 5.

It is impossible to list all pairs of real numbers that add to 5, for there is an infinite number of them. In such a case, we describe the set of all the pairs (x, y) whose sum is 5 in this way:

$$\{(x, y) \mid x + y = 5\}$$

The braces, $\{ \ \}$, show this is a *set*. The parentheses indicate an *ordered pair*. The vertical line, "$\mid$," is read "such that." Thus, the expression means "the set of all ordered pairs x and y, such that $x + y = 5$." The graph of this relation is this:

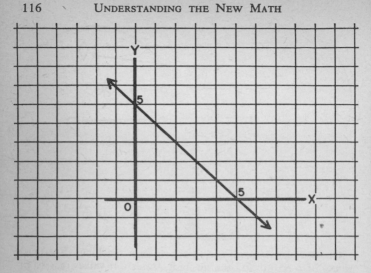

Not only positive integers but also negative, rational, and irrational numbers are used for the x and y values, so long as they add to 5.

The special sort of relationship we usually study is called a *function*. This is another of those words whose mathematical meaning is not like its ordinary non-technical definition. A *function* is a relation in which no two different ordered pairs have the same first member. The arbitrary relation we used on page 114 is not a function, because it contains both (3, 4) and (3, 1), two different pairs with the same first member, 3. When $x = 3$, y is either 4 or 1. In a function this is impossible, because for each x, we want just one value of y. (However, several x's can have the same y.) The other two relations we used on pages 115 and 116 are functions.

There are almost as many definitions of the word *function* as there are mathematicians who feel like making them. In the long run, all have the same meaning, but some are easier to understand than others. For some, a function is a graph (on the Cartesian plane) such that no vertical line cuts it more than once; this last part is to insure that for each x there is only one y. Some describe a function as a rule that prescribes a unique value of y for any given value of x. Others would call it a mapping of one set on another in which no two elements of the second set come from the same element of the first; the first set is called the *domain*, the second the *range*.

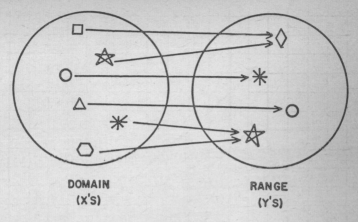

DOMAIN
(X'S)

RANGE
(Y'S)

One way to think of a function is as a machine. You feed values of x into it and the machine grinds out values of y to fit them.

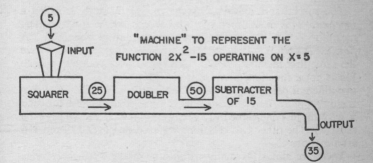

"MACHINE" TO REPRESENT THE FUNCTION $2x^2 - 15$ OPERATING ON $X = 5$

The easiest sort of function to understand is one that can be described by a formula such as $y = x^2$. It is the set of ordered pairs

$$\{(0, 0), (1, 1), (2, 4), (3, 9), (-1, 1), (-2, 4), (-3, 9), \ldots\}$$

or

$$\{(x, y) \mid y = x^2\}$$

or

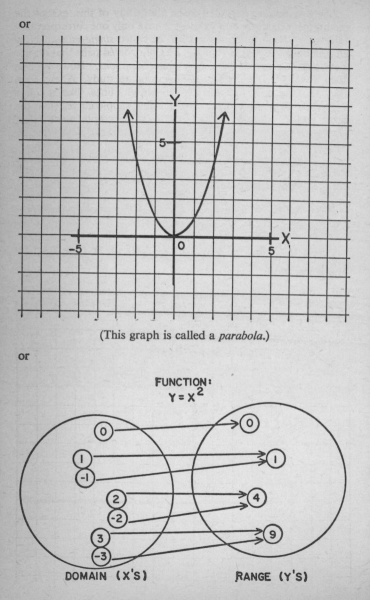

(This graph is called a *parabola*.)

or

FUNCTION:
$Y = X^2$

DOMAIN (X'S)   RANGE (Y'S)

There is nothing especially *new* about any of this, except the requirement that any one value of x have only one corresponding value of y. Such functions used to be called *single-valued*. Now *all* functions are single-valued. Sets of ordered pairs that do not meet this requirement are now called *relations*. However, the main novelty lies in the sort of functions we study. A few years ago, all graphs turned out to be straight lines (like the line $x + y = 5$ on page 116) or one of a few simple curves (like the curve $y = x^2$ on page 118). Now we study graphs made up of separate points (see the graphs on pages 114-115), bent lines, or separate line segments. Let's look at some.

If the sets we are using for both the domain and range are not the set of all the real numbers in some interval, our graph must be made up of separate points. For instance,

$$\{(x, y) \mid y = \sqrt{25 - x^2} \quad \text{and } x \text{ and } y \text{ are integers}\}$$

is the same as

$$\{(0, 5), (3, 4), (-3, 4), (5, 0), (-5, 0), (4, 3), (-4, 3)\}$$

The graph of this function is

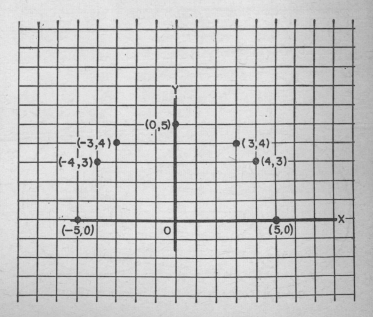

(Although any number has two square roots, the sign $\sqrt{a}$ means the positive number whose square is a. $\sqrt{9} = 3$; $-\sqrt{9} = -3$; $\pm\sqrt{9} = \pm 3$.) $\{(x, y) \mid y = \sqrt{25 - x^2}$ and x is an integer$\}$ contains the same seven points and in addition four others, $(1, \sqrt{24})$, $(-1, \sqrt{24})$, $(2, \sqrt{21})$, and $(-2, \sqrt{21})$, or $(1, 4.90)$, $(-1, 4.90)$, $(2, 4.58)$, and $(-2, 4.58)$. Note that we've used only the integers 1 and 2 for x here because we'd already used 5, 4, 3, and zero. Also note that 6 or larger integers can't be used, since we can't take the square root of a negative number. This graph has eleven separate points.

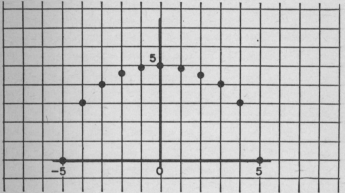

However, $\{(x, y) \mid y = \sqrt{25 - x^2}\}$ is a set with an infinite number of points. Its graph is this semicircle, which illustrates that all the gaps have been filled in.

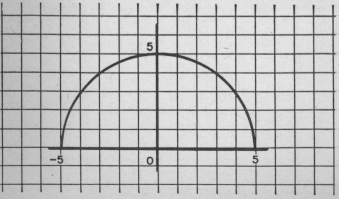

The sort of graph with separate points is frequently more realistic than the traditional kind. For instance, a problem in an old elementary-algebra book might read, "Marbles cost 3¢ apiece. If x = the number of marbles Bill bought, and y = the number of cents he spent on them, write a formula relating x and y, and graph it." The expected and accepted answer was "$y = 3x$" and the following graph:

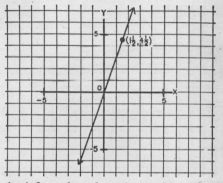

Of course, both formula and graph are misleading if not actually wrong. From them, many nonsensical conclusions can be drawn, such as if $x = 1\frac{1}{2}$, then $y = 4\frac{1}{2}$, and if $x = -6$, then $y = -18$. They are nonsensical in that the formula implies that Bill bought, for example, $1\frac{1}{2}$ marbles and that on another occasion he paid -18 cents for 6 marbles that were not there.

In this problem, both x and y must, of course, be counting numbers. A sensible formula would have to include this fact (by mentioning the domain and range), and the only sensible graph is

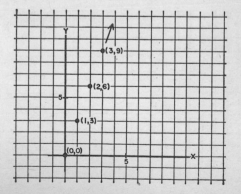

The simplest bent-line graph is that which shows y as the *absolute value* of x. This is written $y = |x|$, and y being the absolute value of x means that y is either x or its additive inverse, whichever is non-negative (see footnote p. 87). For instance,

$$|7| = 7 \quad \text{and} \quad |-7| = 7$$
$$|0| = 0$$
$$|5| = |-5| = 5$$

The graph of the function $y = |x|$ is

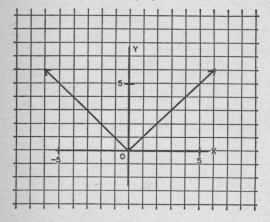

Compare this with the graph of $y = x$:

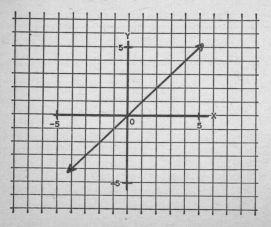

Where $y = x$ is straight and has negative values of y, the function $y = |x|$ has only non-negative values and therefore bends and stays above the x-axis. Graphs of functions involving absolute values usually have corners in them.

A problem for which this sort of graph is appropriate is: "The children in this class walk at the rate of 3 miles per hour. They all live between 1 mile east and 1 mile west of the school on the same road as the school. Draw a graph showing the time it takes to walk to school as a function of the distance east of school." A child who walks 3 miles per hour will walk 1 mile in $\frac{1}{3}$ of an hour, or 20 minutes. If distance east is called positive, distance west must be considered negative, but no child takes a negative number of minutes to reach school.

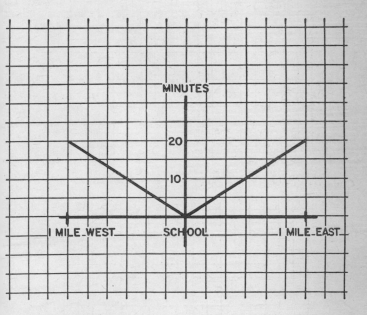

A third new-fangled function is required by old problems like this: "If a taxi charges 25¢ for the first fifth of a mile and 5¢ for each additional fifth of a mile, write and graph a formula for y, the cost in cents, of traveling x fifths of a mile." The old-fashioned answers were $y = 25 + 5(x - 1)$ or $y = 20 + 5x$, and the following graph:

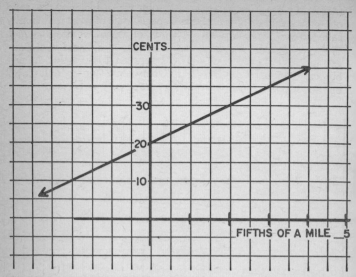

Again, nonsense. If you travel 2½ fifths of a mile, you pay the same as if you'd gone 3 fifths. The meter doesn't creep along continuously; it jumps. The graph should appear as follows:

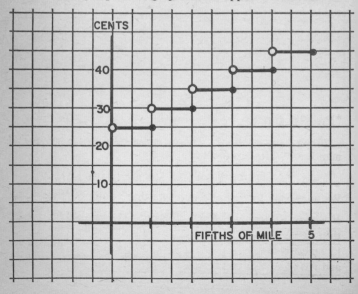

(An empty dot indicates that the point is not included. A solid one indicates that it is.) This is a special case of what is variously called a *bracket function*, *step function*, or *greatest integer function*. "$y = [x]$" means "y is the greatest integer in x," that is, the largest integer not exceeding x. If x is between 1 and 2, including 1 but not including 2, $[x]$ is 1. For x between 2 and 3, including 2 but not 3, $[x] = 2$; and so on. The graph of $y = [x]$ is:

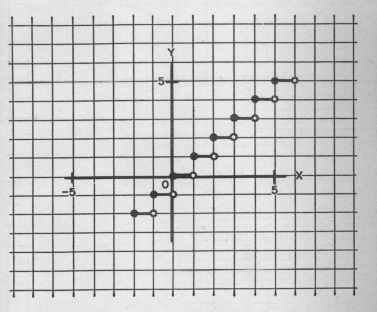

*Problems

Graph these relations. The variables refer to the set of real numbers. Which are functions?

Illustrative example: $|x| - |y| = 1$

We must look for pairs of numbers that fit and tabulate them:

If x is	1 or -1	2 or -2	3 or -3	4 or -4	
then $|x|$ is	1	2	3	4	and so on
$|y|$ must be	0	1	2	3	
and y is	0	1 or -1	2 or -2	3 or -3	

We cannot take zero as a value for x, since $|y|$ would then have to be -1, which is impossible, inasmuch as absolute values can't be negative. When we plot the numbers in the table, we get the following graph:

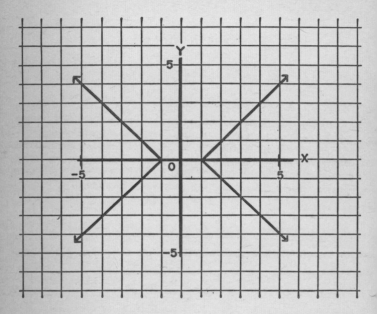

The graphed equation $|x| - |y| = 1$ is *not* a function. For instance, when $x = 2$, y can be 1 or -1. In other words, y has two values corresponding to one value of x, and therefore the equation does not represent a function (see page 116). Moreover, vertical lines that cut it at all cut it twice.

1. $y = \sqrt{x}$ 2. $y^2 = x$

3. $x = |y|$ 4. $y = x^2 - 4$

5. $y = |x^2 - 4|$ 6. $x^2 + y^2 = 25$

7. $|x| + |y| = 5$ *8. $y = |x - 1| + |x + 1|$

*9. $y = x - [x] - \frac{1}{2}$

10. Third-class postal rates are 4¢ for the first 2 ounces and 2¢ for each additional ounce or fraction thereof.

11. $y = 3$

12. $x = 3$

ANSWERS AND EXPLANATIONS

1 and 2. Remember that $\sqrt{x}$ means the positive number whose square is x. $y^2 = x$ means both $y = \sqrt{x}$ and $y = -\sqrt{x}$. Of course x cannot be negative in either of these.

6 and 7. Neither variable can exceed 5. If it did, in Problem 6, the other would be the square root of a negative number. In Problem 7, we would need a negative absolute value.

The graphs in Problems 1, 4, 5, 8, 9, 10, and 11 are functions. In Problems 2, 3, 6, and 7, most x-values have two y-values associated with them, and vertical lines that cut them at all cut them twice. In Problem 12, $x = 3$ goes with all values of y.

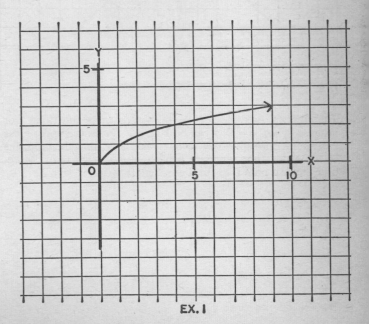

EX. I

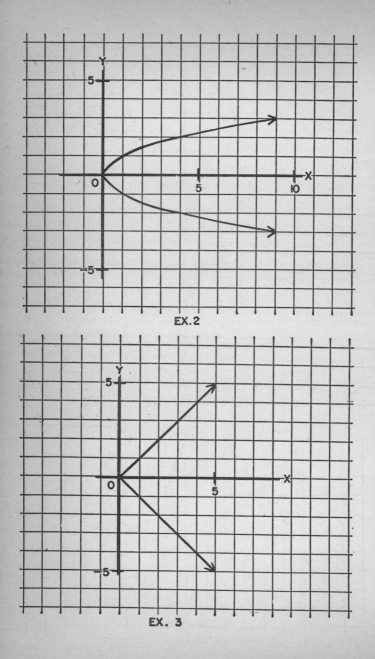

EX.2

EX. 3

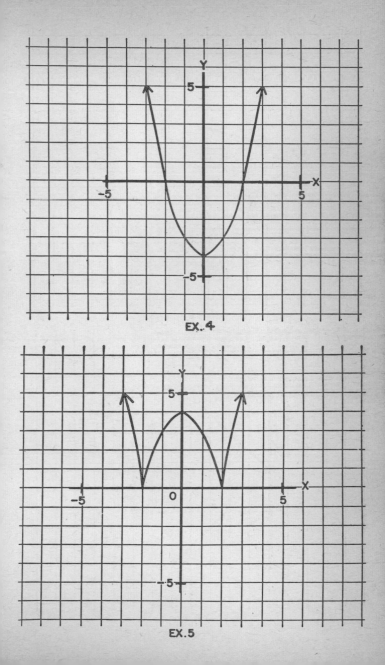

EX. 4

EX. 5

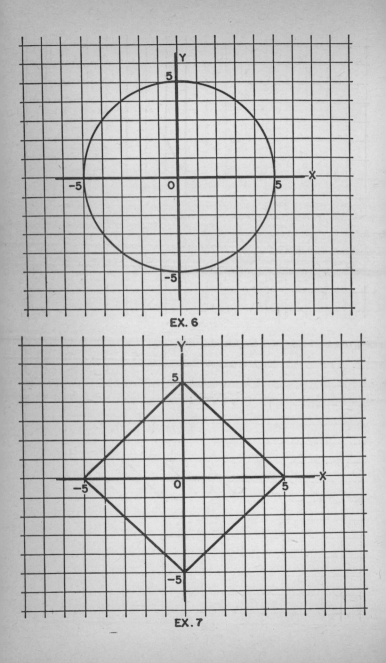

EX. 6

EX. 7

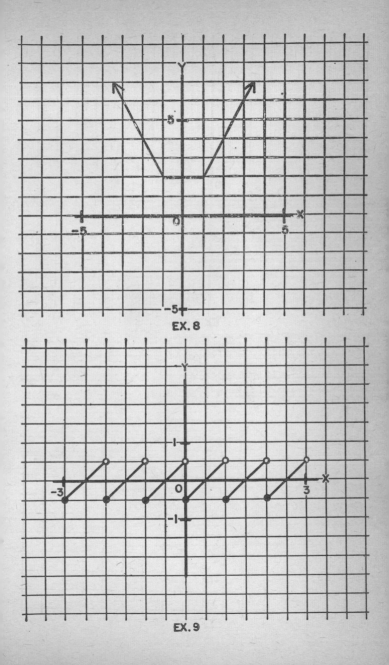

EX. 8

EX. 9

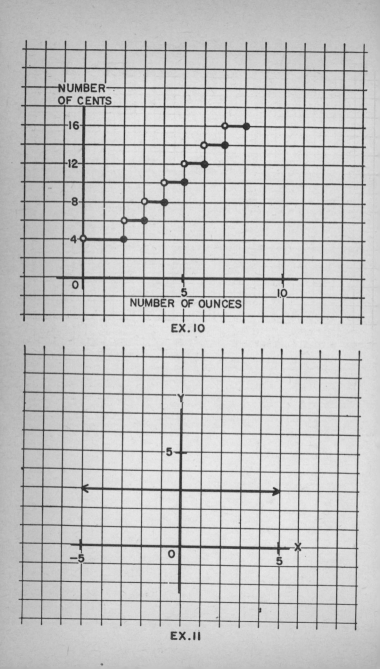

NUMBER
OF CENTS

16

12

8

4

0

5

10

NUMBER OF OUNCES

EX.10

Y

5

−5

0

5

X

EX.11

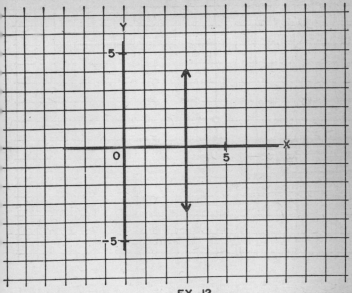

EX. 12

Graphing Solution Sets on the Cartesian Plane

Old style: Solve graphically the simultaneous equations

$$\begin{cases} 3x + 2y = 14 \\ x - y = 3 \end{cases}$$

New style: Find on the Cartesian plane

$$\{(x, y) \mid 3x + 2y = 14 \quad \text{and} \quad x - y = 3\}$$

These are two ways of stating the same problem. Here is its solution:

For each equation, we make a table of some points whose co-ordinates fit it:

$$3x + 2y = 14 \begin{cases} \text{If } x \text{ is} \\ \text{then } y \text{ is} \end{cases}$$

If x is	0	2	4	6
then y is	7	4	1	−2

$$x - y = 3 \begin{cases} \text{If } x \text{ is} \\ \text{then } y \text{ is} \end{cases}$$

If x is	0	3	6	9
then y is	−3	0	3	6

Now we plot these points and draw the graph.

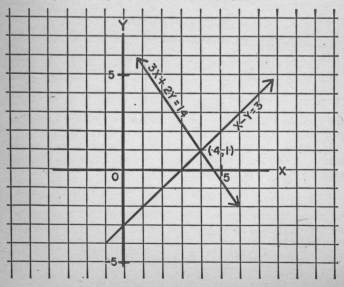

If a point is on a graph, its co-ordinates satisfy the equation represented by the graph. In the graph of the simultaneous equations, the point (4, 1) is not only where the two lines intersect, but it also identifies $x = 4$ and $y = 1$ as a pair of numbers satisfying both equations. It is the only such pair.

Nowadays, in the new math, we find inequalities as important and interesting as equations. The graph of an inequality is not a line but an area.

The inequality $x + y > 5$ is the shaded area above and to

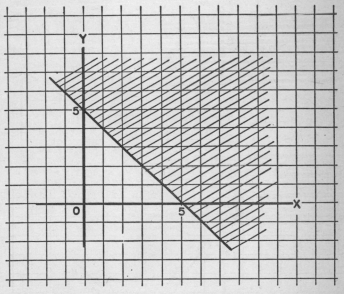

the right of the line $x + y = 5$. In this part of the Cartesian plane, the co-ordinates of any point add to more than 5.

If we want the simultaneous solution of two or more inequalities, we look for the intersection or overlapping of two or more areas. For instance, to find

$$\{(x, y) \mid 3x + 2y > 14 \quad \text{and} \quad x - y < 3\}$$

we graph the solution set of each inequality and look for the portion of the Cartesian plane in both. The vertically shaded area represents

$$\{(x, y) \mid 3x + 2y > 14\}$$

and the horizontally shaded area represents $\{(x, y) \mid x - y < 3\}$. If we are in doubt as to which side of the line we want, the simplest method of making sure is to test a point on either side.

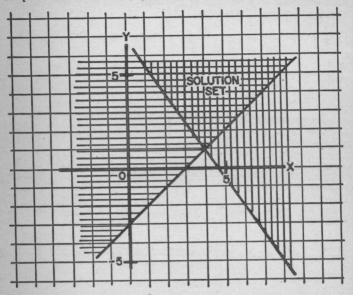

For instance, $(0, 0)$ should not be in the vertically shaded part, because, by substituting zero for x and y in the inequality, we get

$$(3 \times 0) + (2 \times 0) > 14$$

which is false. It should be in the horizontally shaded part, since

$$0 - 0 < 3$$

is true.

The solution set of the pair of inequalities is the part that is shaded both ways, the part labeled "solution set."

*PROBLEMS

On the Cartesian plane, show by shading the solution sets of the inequalities below.

Illustrative example:

$$|x + 2| < 1 \quad \text{and} \quad x^2 + y^2 < 16$$

Remember, while experimenting with substitution into $|x + 2| < 1$, that an absolute value is non-negative (see page 122 and the problems on page 125 and their answers). If the absolute value of a number is less than 1, that number must lie between -1 and 1; therefore,

$|x + 2| < 1$ means that $x + 2$ must be less than 1 and more than -1.

$x + 2 < 1$ means that x must be less than -1.

$x + 2 > -1$ means that x must be more than -3.

Therefore, x must be between -3 and -1. The graph of this is a vertical strip between -3 and -1.

To graph $x^2 + y^2 < 16$, we first make the table for $x^2 + y^2 = 16$.

If x is	0	1 or -1	2 or -2	3 or -3	4 or -4
then x^2 is	0	1	4	9	16
y^2 must be	16	15	12	7	0
and y is	4 or -4	$\sqrt{15}, -\sqrt{15}$ 3.9, -3.9	$\sqrt{12}, -\sqrt{12}$ 3.5, -3.5	$\sqrt{7}, -\sqrt{7}$ 2.6, -2.6	0

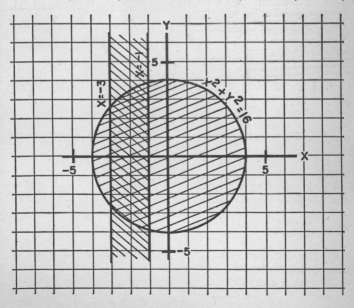

These points are on a circle. We want points where $x^2 + y^2 <$ 16. We want, therefore, the interior of the circle. The solution set of each inequality is shaded; the solution set of the pair of inequalities is shaded both ways.

1. $2x + y < 4$ and $5x - y < 17$

2. $x^2 + y^2 > 9$ and $x^2 + y^2 < 25$

3. $y > x^2$ and $y < 2x + 3$

*4. $|x| + |y| < 4$ and $|y - 2| < 1$

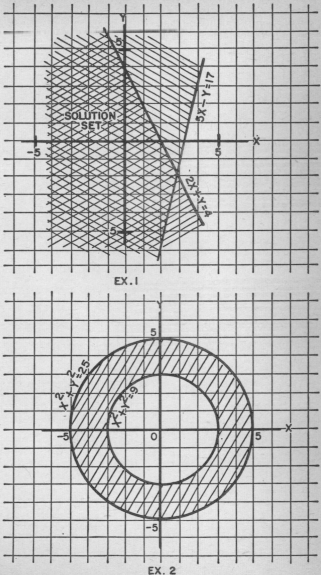

EX. 1

EX. 2

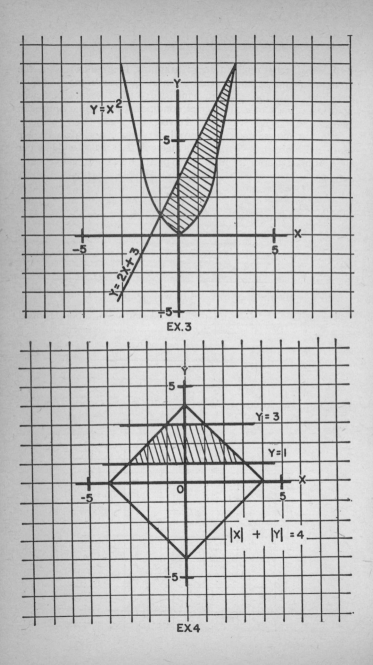

EX.3

EX4

Linear Programming

A very pretty application of graphing inequalities is in the branch of mathematics called linear programming. Many practical problems arise in which we want the most efficient solution subject to a number of conditions; a graphic approach helps. To clarify what is involved, consider this problem:

A manufacturer makes two products, gadgets and widgets. He can't sell more than 5 cases of gadgets or 3 cases of widgets per day. It takes 1 hour for his plant to produce a case of gadgets and 2 hours to produce a case of widgets. The plant operates 8 hours a day. He has enough material to make not more than 6 cases of both together per day. If the profits on gadgets are $20 per case and on widgets $30 per case, how should he plan his daily production?

So much information is given here that it is hard to absorb and use it all. Let's try to translate it into mathematical language:

Let x = the number of cases of gadgets per day

and y = the number of cases of widgets per day.

Then $\left.\begin{array}{l} x \geq 0 \\ y \geq 0 \end{array}\right\}$ He can't produce a negative number of cases of either.

$\left.\begin{array}{l} x \leq 5 \\ y \leq 3 \end{array}\right\}$ He won't make more than he can sell.

$x + 2y \leq 8$ Time is limited to 8 hours a day.

$x + y \leq 6$ Material is limited to 6 cases a day.

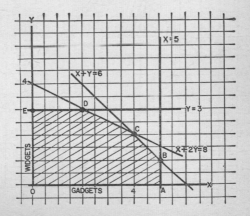

Profits: $20x + 30y$. He wants this to be as large as possible, subject to all the above requirements. If we graph all the inequalities, we find the shaded area as the solution set. The coordinates of any point in or on the boundary of that area will meet the limitations. Which gives the manufacturer the greatest profit?

Let us try several:

Point	Location	Value of $20x + 30y$
(2,1)	Inside	70
(4,1)	Inside	110
(2,2)	Inside	100
(1,3)	On side DE	110
$(3,2\frac{1}{3})$	On side CD	135
$(4\frac{1}{2},1\frac{1}{2})$	On side BC	135
(0,0)	Vertex 0	0
(5,0)	Vertex A	100
(5,1)	Vertex B	130
(4,2)	Vertex C	140
(2,3)	Vertex D	130
(0,3)	Vertex E	90

Notice that both the largest value (140) and the smallest value (0) occur at vertices. It can be proved that this is generally true, so that we can test only those points. In this case, then, the manufacturer should make 4 cases of gadgets and 2 of widgets per day.

Suppose the profits on each case of widgets had been $60. Would his best operation be any different? Our graph and the solution set of the inequalities are the same, but the profit now is $20x + 60y$ dollars.

Vertex	x	y	$20x + 60y$	
0	0	0	0	Minimum again
A	5	0	100	
B	5	1	160	
C	4	2	200	
D	2	3	220	Maximum
E	0	3	180	

Now he should produce 2 cases of gadgets and 3 of widgets, even though this does not use up all his available material.

*PROBLEMS

1. Machine X can produce 100 boxes of nails and 40 boxes of tacks per hour. Machine Y can produce 50 boxes of nails and 70 boxes of tacks per hour. At least 500 boxes of each must be produced. The total time on the two machines together cannot exceed 11 hours. If it costs $2 per hour to run machine X and $3 per hour to run machine Y, how many hours should each operate? Would it make a difference if Y cost $4 per hour?

2. A retailer bought two different mixtures of nuts. The "special" mixture contains 2 ounces of pecans, 1 ounce of cashews, and 1 ounce of almonds in each pound. The "fancy" mixture contains 1 ounce of pecans, 2 ounces of cashews, and 6 ounces of almonds in each pound. The rest of each mixture is peanuts. The retailer wants to make up large boxes containing at least 8 ounces of pecans, 10 ounces of cashews, and 18 ounces of almonds. How much of each mixture should he use if the "special" costs $1 per pound and the "fancy" $1.50 per pound? If the "special" costs $1 per pound and the "fancy" $2.50 per pound?

3. Mr. Smith takes two brands of vitamin pills. He refuses to take more than 6 pills a day. Their content and the minimum daily needs in milligrams are listed below:

	Thiamin	Riboflavin	Niacin
Vim	1	1	10
Vigor	1	2	5
Daily Requirements	3	4	20

If Vim costs 4¢ per pill and Vigor 9¢ per pill, how many of each should Mr. Smith take? How many, if Vim costs 10¢ per pill and Vigor 6¢?

ANSWERS AND EXPLANATIONS

1. Let x = number of hours machine X operates

and y = number of hours machine Y operates.

Then $x \geq 0$ and $y \geq 0$.

$\left.\begin{array}{l} 100x + 50y \geq 500 \\ 40x + 70y \geq 500 \end{array}\right\}$ To produce at least 500 boxes of each.

$$x + y \leq 11 \quad \text{Limitation on time.}$$

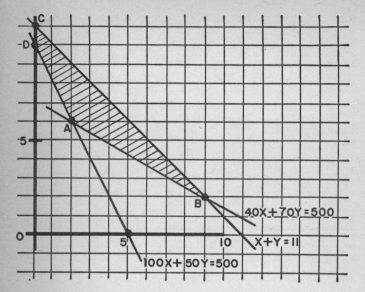

			Cost	
Vertex	x	y	$2x + 3y$	$2x + 4y$
A	2	6	22	28	Best if Y costs $3 per hour
B	9	2	24	26	Best if Y costs $4 per hour
C	0	11	33	44	Most expensive, both ways
D	0	10	30	40	

Therefore, at $2 and $3 per hour, X should run 2 and Y should run 6 hours. At $2 and $4, X should run 9 and Y should run 2 hours.

2. Let x = number of pounds of "special"

and y = number of pounds of "fancy."

Then $x \geq 0$ and $y \geq 0$.

$$2x + y \geq 8 \qquad \text{To get enough pecans.}$$
$$x + 2y \geq 10 \qquad \text{To get enough cashews.}$$
$$x + 6y \geq 18 \qquad \text{To get enough almonds.}$$

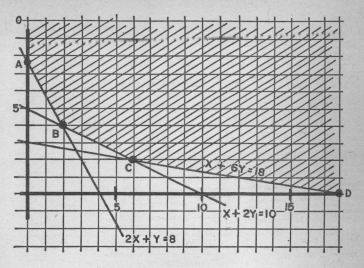

Vertex	x	y	Cost $x + 1\frac{1}{2}y$	$x + 2\frac{1}{2}y$	
A	0	8	12	20	Worst, 2nd way
B	2	4	8	12	Best, 1st way
C	6	2	9	11	Best, 2nd way
D	18	0	18	18	Worst, 1st way

Therefore, at \$1 and \$1.50 per pound, respectively, he should use 2 pounds of "special" and 4 of "fancy." At \$1 and \$2.50, respectively, he should use 6 pounds of "special" and 2 pounds of "fancy."

3. Let x = number of Vim pills per day

and y = number of Vigor pills per day.

Then $x \geq 0$ and $y \geq 0$.

$$\begin{aligned} x + y &\geq 3 & \text{To get enough thiamin.} \\ x + 2y &\geq 4 & \text{To get enough riboflavin.} \\ 10x + 5y &\geq 20 & \text{To get enough niacin.} \\ x + y &\leq 6 & \text{To keep under his maximum.} \end{aligned}$$

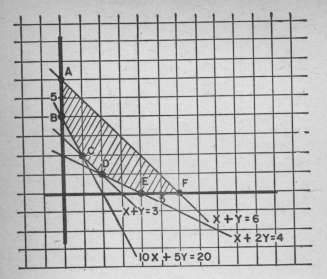

			Cost		
Vertex	x	y	$4x + 9y$	$10x + 6y$	
A	0	6	54	36	Worst, 1st way
B	0	4	36	24	
C	1	2	22	22	Best, 2nd way
D	2	1	17	26	
E	4	0	16	40	Best, 1st way
F	6	0	24	60	Worst, 2nd way

Therefore, at 4¢ apiece for Vim and 9¢ apiece for Vigor, Mr. Smith should take 4 Vim pills only. At 10¢ and 6¢, respectively, he should take 1 Vim and 2 Vigor pills.

There is also a similar process called *non-linear programming*. The diagram on p. 147, referring to the cost of operating an oil refinery for various combinations of temperature and pressure, appeared in a booklet, *Careers in Mathematics*, put out by the National Council of Teachers of Mathematics and the National Academy of Sciences—National Research Council.

The idea of plotting points and graphing equations goes back more than three hundred years and is certainly not new in mathematics. The newness lies in the sort of relations we plot.

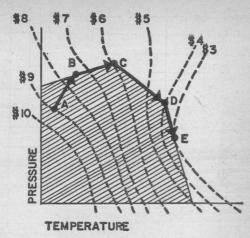

This miniature example of nonlinear programming portrays the search for a combination of temperature and pressure within the shaded region that lies on the lowest cost line. Starting at A the computing machine would follow the path shown to the answer E.

If you look at any traditional textbook, you will not find diagrams like most of those in this chapter. Graphs of equations showing separate points, separate line segments, or bent lines, and graphs of inequalities showing areas are often more interesting and useful than the straight lines and simple curves that fill classical mathematics.

SECTION IV
Sets and Logic

Most of the new mathematics consists of a new approach to various traditional branches of mathematics. The timing may be different. At present, children might begin the study of algebra and geometry in elementary school. That is, algebra may be begun in fourth or fifth grade and intuitive geometry in first grade. The emphasis may be different. In arithmetic and algebra there may be more stress on the structure of the system and on its abstract foundations. However, the material is still arithmetic and algebra and geometry, and its essentials are recognizable, if not readily comprehensible, to anyone who ever went through high school.

Not so with the topics of *sets* and *logic*. These are completely new subjects as far as pre-college courses go. Yet the elements of mathematical logic are now found in many high-school courses, and sets are used all the way from kindergarten through graduate school. The two topics are closely related. The simplest approach to logic is through sets. It seems inevitable to find both of them included together in the new curricula.

The idea of a set, or class of things, is, of course, not a new one. A *herd* of cows, a *swarm* of bees, a *flock* of birds, a *troop* of Boy Scouts, a *chain* of stores, and a stamp *collection* are all instances of sets. There is nothing recondite about the basic notion. At first sight it even seems obvious and trivial. It turns out to be neither.

Not only mathematicians but also scientists and social scientists in many fields now think in terms of sets. For instance, in the insurance business, any one person cannot be dealt with on an individual basis, but sets of people in a given age-group can be handled easily. In most statistical work with large numbers, sets, not individuals, are used. It is easy to visualize sets with a small number of elements in them—the set of girls in the class or the set of cards in a deck. It gets a bit harder if we have a very large set—the set of all the people in the world or the set of all natural numbers.

It turns out that there are many sorts of problems that can be solved by thinking in terms of sets. Here is one: Show that if no one has more than one million hairs on his head, then at least two people in New York City must have the same number of hairs on their heads.

Solution: Pair off each individual in New York City with the counting number, 0, 1, 2, . . . 1,000,000, that represents the number of hairs he has on his head. Since there are more than 1,000,001 people in New York City, we will run out of numbers before we run out of people, so that at least two people must be paired with the same number. This depends on the idea of trying to set up a one-to-one correspondence between sets. We discussed one-to-one correspondence in Chapter 7 (pages 105 and 106). The solutions of other sorts of problems depend on other ideas relating to sets, which we will take up in Chapter 9.

Philosophers and logicians usually assert that mathematics is part of logic. Mathematicians see it the other way around and assert that logic is part of mathematics. It certainly is part of mathematics courses today. Sections on logic can be found in many high-school textbooks on both algebra and geometry. It is useful in both subjects, as well as in many academic and non-academic fields.

Many successes of civilized man are due to his ability to use logical reasoning. Many of his failures are due to the lack of this ability. Enterprises that are carried out logically are often complimented by being compared to mathematics: it is said that they are conducted with mathematical precision. The physical sciences are called exact sciences, because they can be expressed in mathematical terms. The social sciences sometimes attempt the same kind of formulation. Even morality and philosophy can aspire to be completely logical by being mathematical. For example, Spinoza asserted that his *Ethics* was "demonstrated according to the geometrical manner."

The ability to reason logically distinguishes intelligent men from all others. (A question that often arises from this is "Since computers make logical decisions, are they intelligent?") The ability to reason is partly innate, but it can certainly be cultivated and improved. By studying some of the logical principles that govern deductive reasoning, we are trying to do this.

Chapter 9
More About Sets

The idea of sets is an underlying one in mathematics. Several new symbols are needed to describe their relations. We can picture sets and operations with these symbols in many ways. There are axioms that govern the *union* and *intersection* of sets, which correspond roughly to addition and multiplication of numbers. Many problems can be visualized and solved by means of *set diagrams*.

New Words and Symbols

When we first mentioned the word *set*, we said it means merely a collection of any sort of objects. All the sets we've examined so far, however, have been sets of numbers or of pairs of numbers. Here we shall look at other sets and at the symbols used in discussing them.

Suppose we have the set A = {Ann, Bob, Charles, Dorothy}. Ann is a member, or *element*, of the set. There are four elements altogether in the set.

If B is the set of boys in A, then B is {Bob, Charles}, and B is known as a *subset* of A, written as

$$B \subset A$$

This means that any element in B is also in A. Oddly enough, by this definition it turns out that A is a subset of itself,

$$A \subset A$$

since any member of A is, of course, in A. To make it clear that B is a different sort of subset and that the "sub" in *subset* means something here, we may call B a *proper* subset of A. This means that there are some elements of A not in B.

(If there are two sets, P and Q, such that each is a subset of the other,

$$P \subset Q \quad \text{and} \quad Q \subset P$$

then they must be identical, since any element in either is also in the other.)

Let's consider, along with sets A and B, set C. Set C is to be the set of all camels in A. Obviously, there are none; so C is { }, called the *empty set* or the *null set* and usually indicated by ∅. Moreover, C ⊂ A, since anything that is in C is also in A. As there is nothing in C, it is easy for this to be true. In fact, it is true no matter what set A is: ∅ is a subset of every set.

∅ is not the same as 0 or as {0}. 0 is not a set, but ∅ and {0} are. However, {0} is a set containing one element, 0, and ∅ is { }, the set with no elements.

How many subsets can a set have? Let's consider sets of 1, 2, or 3 elements.

(1) {Ann} has subsets {Ann} and { }, or ∅.

(2) {Ann, Bob} has subsets {Ann, Bob}, {Ann}, {Bob}, and ∅.

(3) {Ann, Bob, Charles} has subsets {Ann, Bob, Charles}, {Ann, Bob}, {Ann, Charles}, {Bob, Charles}, {Ann}, {Bob}, {Charles}, and ∅.

> 1 element —2 subsets
> 2 elements—4 subsets
> 3 elements—8 subsets

It should be fairly easy to see the pattern. If we consider the subsets of {Ann, Bob, Charles, Dorothy}, we can take each of the 8 subsets of {Ann, Bob, Charles} and either put Dorothy in or leave her out, making 16 subsets in all. For a set of n elements, there are 2^n subsets.

Let's look at these two sets:

$$V = \{a, e, i, o, u\} \quad \text{and} \quad F = \{a, b, c, d, e, f\}$$

These sets have as elements letters of the English alphabet. Let's use this alphabet for our *universal set* or *universe* U for this discussion. V is the set of vowels and F the set of first letters up to and including f. These two sets immediately suggest other sets: the consonants; the set {a, e}, made up of letters in both of the original sets; and so on. All these can be described in terms of V and F. Let us see how.

The set of all consonants, that is, the non-vowels, in the alphabet is called the *complement* of V, and it is written V′. Similarly, F′ is the complement of F, or the set of all those members of U not in F. In other words, F′ is the set of the last twenty letters of the alphabet, from g to z.

The complement of the universal set, everything not in it, is the empty set, Ø. The complement of the empty set, everything not in it (that is, everything), is the universal set.

$$U' = \emptyset \qquad \emptyset' = U$$

{a, e}, the set made up of those elements in both V and F, is called the *intersection* of V and F, written V ∩ F, and sometimes read—nonsensically enough—as "V cap F." This use of the word *intersection* comes naturally from its geometric meaning. Each line is a set of points; and P, the point on both lines (in both sets), is the intersection of the two sets.

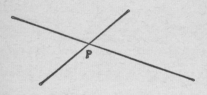

{a, b, c, d, e, f, i, o, u}, the set of those elements in either V or F or both, is called the *union* of V and F, written V ∪ F, and sometimes read "V cup F." (Note that in mathematics the expression *either—or* regularly includes the idea *both*.)

Flippant students call set theory *cups and caps*.

These symbols can be combined in various ways. For instance, {i, o, u} is V ∩ F', the letters that are both vowels and not in the first six letters.

The order in which we write the elements of a set does not matter. That is, {a, e} and {e, a} are the same. Thus

$$V \cup F = F \cup V \quad \text{and} \quad V \cap F = F \cap V$$

Here are two other sets: B is the set of girls at the party that the boys considered beautiful and C is the set they considered clever:

$$B = \{Ann, Betty, Claire, Flo\}$$

$$C = \{Betty, Dora, Flo\}$$

There were seven girls at the party. No one thought that Edna or Grace had either asset.

U here, our universe, is the set of all the girls at the party.

U = {Ann, Betty, Claire, Dora, Edna, Flo, Grace}

B $\cup$ C, the union of B and C, is the set of girls in either B or C, those with at least one asset.

B $\cup$ C = {Ann, Betty, Claire, Dora, Flo}

B $\cap$ C, the intersection of B and C, is the set of girls in both B and C, those with both advantages.

B $\cap$ C = {Betty, Flo}

B′ is the set of non-beautiful girls, {Dora, Edna, Grace}.
C′ is the set of non-clever girls, {Ann, Claire, Edna, Grace}.

(B $\cup$ C)′ means the set of girls at the party who are *not* either beautiful or clever. Of course, this is the same as the set of those who are both not beautiful and not clever, B′ $\cap$ C′. We can find (B $\cup$ C)′ by starting with U and removing B $\cup$ C.

{Ann, Betty, Claire, Dora, Edna, Flo, Grace}

B′ $\cap$ C′ is the set of those in both B′ and C′. Either way,

(B $\cup$ C)′ = B′ $\cap$ C′ = {Edna, Grace}

(B $\cap$ C)′ is the set of those who don't have both assets. (B $\cap$ C)′ is the same as B′ $\cup$ C′, those who are either not beautiful or not clever. If we delete B $\cap$ C from U,

{Ann, Betty, Claire, Dora, Edna, Flo, Grace}

or join B′ and C′ (not listing twice any who are in both) we get (B $\cap$ C)′ = B′ $\cup$ C′ = {Ann, Claire, Dora, Edna, Grace}.

All of this information can be presented much more simply and compactly in a diagram like this, called a *Venn diagram*.

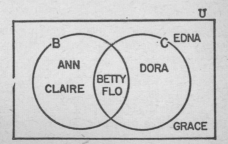

There are a lot of new symbols and concepts in this section.

(1) Subset: $\subset$
(2) The empty set: $\emptyset$
(3) The complement of set A: A'
(4) The universal set: U
(5) The union of sets A and B: $A \cup B$
(6) The intersection of sets A and B: $A \cap B$

As this is the language we will be using for the rest of this chapter, if you haven't absorbed it, you will find it hard to go on—*verb. sap.*, a word to the wise.

PROBLEMS

1. (a) From the diagram on page 153, find $B \cap C'$ and interpret its meaning.
   (b) Who is or are in $B' \cap C$?

2. How many different sums of money can you form from a penny, a nickel, a dime, a quarter, and a half-dollar?

3. The girls at the party talked about the boys, too. They decided that Art, Bill, Chuck, Dan, and Ed were fun to talk to, while Chuck, Dan, George, and Hank were good dancers. No one had anything good to say about Fred. Draw a Venn diagram, using C for the set of good conversationalists and D for the set of good dancers. Then find and describe these subsets:

   (a) $C \cup D$ (b) $C \cap D$ (c) $C' \cup D'$ (d) $C' \cap D'$
   (e) $(C \cup D)'$ (f) $(C \cap D)'$ (g) $C \cap D'$
   (h) $C' \cup D$ (i) $(C \cap D')'$

ANSWERS AND EXPLANATIONS

1. (a) Ann and Claire. They are beautiful and not clever.
   (b) Dora. She is clever and not beautiful.

2. 32, if zero is considered as a sum of money; otherwise 31 different sums of money may be formed. This is just the number of subsets that can be formed from a set of 5 elements, the 5 coins. $2^5 = 32$.

3.

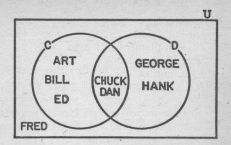

(a) $C \cup D$ = {Art, Bill, Ed, Chuck, Dan, George, Hank}—everyone who has either asset.

(b) $C \cap D$ = {Chuck, Dan} — the fortunate fellows with both.

(c) $C' \cup D'$
(f) $(C \cap D)'$ } = {Art, Bill, Ed, George, Hank, Fred}. They are *either* not good conversationalists *or* not good dancers. That is, they are not *both* good conversationalists *and* good dancers.

(d) $C' \cap D'$
(e) $(C \cup D)'$ } = {Fred}. The poor boy is *both* not a good conversationalist *and* not a good dancer. That is, he is not *either* a good conversationalist *or* a good dancer.

(g) $C \cap D'$ = {Art, Bill, Ed}. They can talk and they can't dance.

(h) $C' \cup D$
(i) $(C \cap D')'$ } = {Chuck, Dan, Fred, George, Hank}, the complement of the set in (g). They *either* are not good conversationalists *or* they are good dancers. That is, they are not *both* good conversationalists *and* poor dancers.

The Relation Between Two Sets

The Venn diagrams on the next page are for complements, union, and intersection: The relation between two sets in each instance is illustrated by the shading.

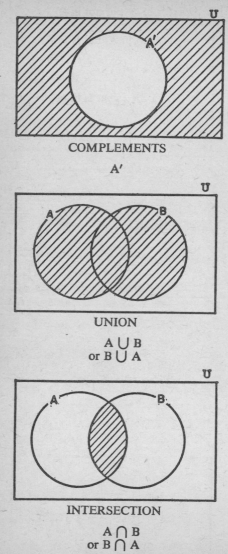

COMPLEMENTS

A'

UNION

A ∪ B
or B ∪ A

INTERSECTION

A ∩ B
or B ∩ A

We can always picture two sets as if they overlapped. The four parts of the diagram immediately following are:

(1) A $\cap$ B' (what is in A and not in B)

(2) A' $\cap$ B (what is not in A, but is in B)

(3) A $\cap$ B (what is in both)

(4) A' $\cap$ B' or (A $\cup$ B)' (what is in neither)

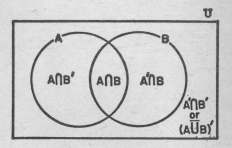

Sometimes this might be misleading. If, for instance, A $\subset$ B, then anything in A is also in B, and A $\cap$ B' is therefore empty. In this case, a better diagram might be

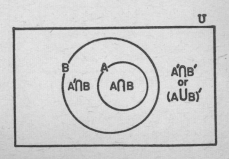

Note that (1) if $A \cup B = A$, then $B \subset A$;

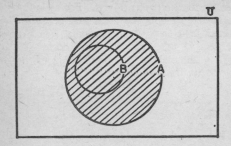

and (2) if $A \cap B = A$, then $A \subset B$.

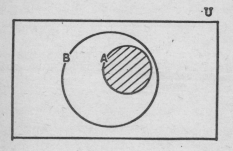

If A and B are separate, or *disjoint* sets, then $A \cap B = \emptyset$. In this case, a better diagram is

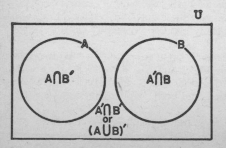

However, we can use the diagram with overlapping circles without confusion if we put the number of elements belonging in each set in the area representing it. For instance, the following Venn diagram represents the facts and provides the answer to the question. In a class of 28 students, 7 take physics, 9 take chemistry, and 12 take neither. How many take both? Since $7 + 9 + 12 = 28$, there is no overlapping of the sets P, those

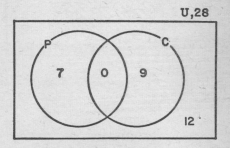

taking physics, and C, those taking chemistry. The diagram shows that P and C are disjoint, since $P \cap C$ is empty, for no student takes both subjects.

PROBLEMS

1. Find (a) $A \cup \emptyset$ (b) $A \cap \emptyset$ (c) $A \cup U$

 (d) $A \cap U$ (e) $U \cup \emptyset$ (f) $U \cap \emptyset$

2. Twelve out of fifty boys in a class take no part in varsity sports. Twenty-seven are on the football team, and eighteen are on the basketball team. Draw a Venn diagram, and use it to answer these questions. How many are on both teams? How many play only football? only basketball?

3. Smithtown, population 2000, has two newspapers, *The Village Views* and *The Town Talk*. Twelve hundred people read *The Views* and nine hundred read *The Talk*. Four hundred read both. How many read neither?

*4. Here is a proof, using Venn diagrams, that $(P \cup Q)' = P' \cap Q'$.

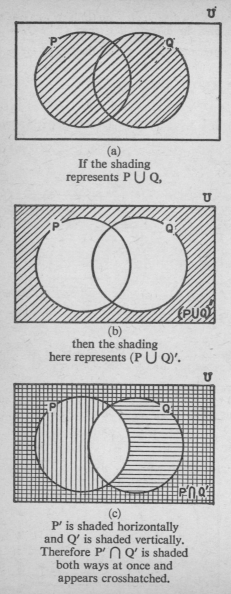

(a)
If the shading
represents P ∪ Q,

(b)
then the shading
here represents (P ∪ Q)′.

(c)
P′ is shaded horizontally
and Q′ is shaded vertically.
Therefore P′ ∩ Q′ is shaded
both ways at once and
appears crosshatched.

Since the shaded area in diagram (b) is the same as the cross-hatched area in diagram (c), then $(P \cup Q)' = P' \cap Q'$.

Use the same method to prove that $(P \cap Q)' = P' \cup Q'$.

ANSWERS AND EXPLANATIONS

1. (a) $A \cup \emptyset = A$ (b) $A \cap \emptyset = \emptyset$ (c) $A \cup U = U$

    (d) $A \cap U = A$ (e) $U \cup \emptyset = U$ (f) $U \cap \emptyset = \emptyset$

2. Only 38 boys are on teams, but $27 + 18 = 45$, so we must have an overlap of 7 boys.

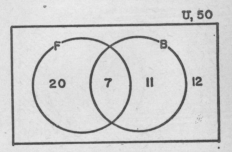

$F \cup B$ has 38 elements and $F \cap B$ has 7. Seven are on both teams. Twenty play only football. Eleven play only basketball.

3. We must put the 400 ($V \cap T$) in the diagram first and then the 800 (or $1200 - 400$) and the 500 (or $900 - 400$). This accounts for 1700 readers. The remaining 300 read neither paper.

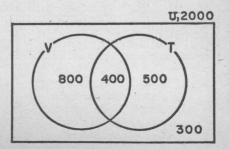

*4.

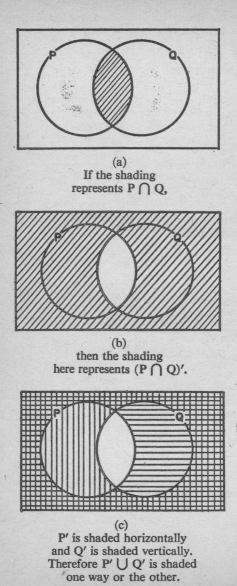

(a)
If the shading
represents P ∩ Q,

(b)
then the shading
here represents (P ∩ Q)′.

(c)
P′ is shaded horizontally
and Q′ is shaded vertically.
Therefore P′ ∪ Q′ is shaded
one way or the other.

Since the shaded area in diagram (b) is the same as in diagram (c), then $(P \cap Q)' = P' \cup Q'$.

Venn Diagrams for Three Sets

We can easily show the union and intersection of three sets in a Venn diagram. (For four sets, it is possible but awkward.) The three sets can be pictured in this way:

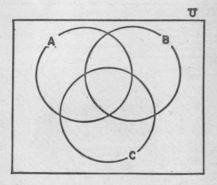

Here, what do we mean by $A \cup B \cup C$? Is it $(A \cup B) \cup C$ or $A \cup (B \cup C)$? It means both, since these are the same. If we unite A and B, and then join C to this, we get everything in any of the three circles. We get the same result if we start by joining B and C, and then unite this with A.

What about $A \cap B \cap C$? If we start with $A \cap B$, the part common to A and B, and then take the portion of that also in C, we get the same area as if we started by taking the overlap of B and C, and then the overlap of that with A. Thus, $(A \cap B) \cap C = A \cap (B \cap C)$.

Note that $\cup$ and $\cap$ are something like $+$ and $\times$ in that they are commutative and associative.

$$A \cup B = B \cup A$$
$$(A \cup B) \cup C = A \cup (B \cup C)$$
$$A \cap B = B \cap A$$
$$(A \cap B) \cap C = A \cap (B \cap C)$$

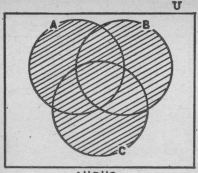

A∪B∪C

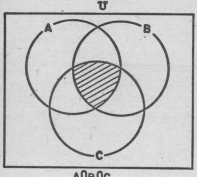

A∩B∩C

We can find out if the distributive law holds by checking in the diagram. There are, however, two possible distributive laws. For numbers

$$a \times (b + c) = (a \times b) + (a \times c)$$

but

$$a + (b \times c) \neq (a + b) \times (a + c)$$

Here, with sets, we might have

$$A \cap (B \cup C) = (A \cap B) \cup (A \cap C) \qquad (1)$$

or

$$A \cup (B \cap C) = (A \cup B) \cap (A \cup C) \qquad (2)$$

Let's investigate both:

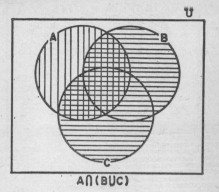

A ∩ (B∪C)

(B ∪ C) is shaded horizontally.
A is shaded vertically.
A ∩ (B ∪ C) is shaded both ways
at once and appears crosshatched.

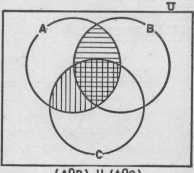

(A∩B) ∪ (A∩C)

A ∩ B is shaded horizontally.
A ∩ C is shaded vertically.
(A ∩ B) ∪ (A ∩ C) is shaded
horizontally or vertically or
both ways at once.

Since these diagrams show the same area, the first distributive law holds.

Now for the second.

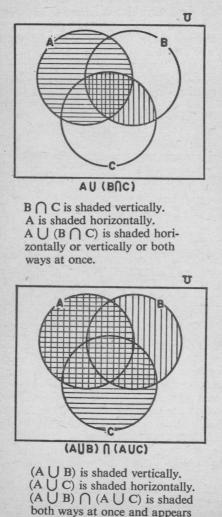

A ∪ (B∩C)

B ∩ C is shaded vertically.
A is shaded horizontally.
A ∪ (B ∩ C) is shaded horizontally or vertically or both ways at once.

(A∪B) ∩ (A∪C)

(A ∪ B) is shaded vertically.
(A ∪ C) is shaded horizontally.
(A ∪ B) ∩ (A ∪ C) is shaded both ways at once and appears crosshatched.

Again, the final result is the same, so this distributive law holds also. Thus we have two distributive laws for union and intersection of sets.

We can use these three-ring diagrams to solve problems with rather involved data. For instance, let's go back to Problem 2 on page 159. Suppose out of the 50 boys, 27 play football, 16 play basketball, and 18 are on the track team; 8 play football and basketball, 3 are on the basketball and track teams, 7 are on the football and track teams, and 3 are on all 3 teams. How many are on no team? How many play only basketball? How many are on the basketball and track teams but not on the football team?

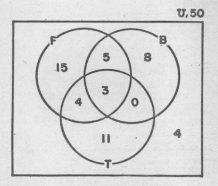

We fill in the numbers the only way we can, beginning at the inmost section, the 3 who are in all three sports. Next we use the numbers for those who are in each combination of two sports, putting the 5, 0, and 4 in the appropriate sections. Next the figures for each sport itself; for instance, to have 27 playing football, we need 15 playing football only $(15 + 5 + 3 + 4 = 27)$. Finally, we see we have accounted for 46 of the 50 boys, leaving 4 outside of all three sets.

Therefore, 4 are on no team, 8 play only basketball, and no one on both the basketball and track teams does not also play football.

Here is another illustration: Three sports writers made the following predictions about which teams would win in four games to be played the next day: Black picked the Aces, Bisons, Colts, and Dukes. Grey picked the Bisons, Colts, Lions, and Sox.

White picked the Colts, Dukes, Lions, and Tigers. Nobody thought the Kings would win. How were the teams paired?

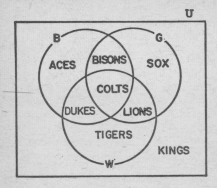

We ask, "Has any one team been picked by all three writers?" All three picked the Colts, so we fill this team in first—in the inner section. Similarly, we ask which teams were picked by two writers. Black and Grey picked the Bisons. Grey and White picked the Lions. Black and White picked the Dukes. Only Black picked the Aces, and so on. Since a writer cannot pick as winners two teams who play each other, the Colts could not, for instance, be playing the Tigers, since White picked both of them. Similarly, the Bisons could not be playing the Sox, since Grey picked both. Continuing in this way, we find that the Colts play the Kings. The Bisons (picked by Black and Grey) play the Tigers (picked by White). The Lions play the Aces; and the Sox play the Dukes.

PROBLEMS

*1. Describe the sets indicated by the shading:

(a)   (b)

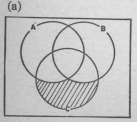
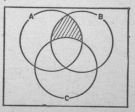

(c)   (d)

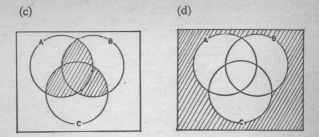

2. If U is the set of integers from 1 to 10 inclusive, E the set of even numbers, P the set of prime numbers, and Q the set of multiples of 4, draw the Venn diagram and find

(a) $P \cap E$ (b) $E \cap Q$ (c) $E \cup Q$

(d) $P \cup Q$ (e) $P \cap Q$ (f) $P \cap E'$

(g) $P' \cap E' \cap Q'$

3. A staff member at an engineering school was presenting data to show that the students there got a liberal education as well as a scientific one. "Look at the record," he said. "Out of our senior class of 500 students, 281 are taking English, 196 are taking history, 286 are taking a foreign language, 64 are taking English and history, 87 are taking history and a foreign language, 143 are taking a foreign language and English, and 36 are taking all three." It sounded most impressive, but he was fired. Why?

ANSWERS AND EXPLANATIONS

*1. (a) $C \cap A' \cap B'$ or $C \cap (A \cup B)'$

(b) $A \cap B \cap C'$

(c) $(A \cap B) \cup (A \cap C) \cup (B \cap C)$

(d) $(A \cup B \cup C)'$ or $A' \cap B' \cap C'$

2.

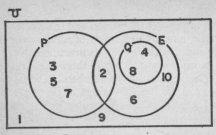

Note that $Q \subset E$.

(a) $P \cap E = \{2\}$

(b) $E \cap Q = \{4, 8\} = Q$

Note that the intersection of E and Q contains all the elements that are in Q, which is the set of multiples of 4 in the integers from 1 to 10.

(c) $E \cup Q = \{2, 4, 6, 8, 10\} = E$

Note that the union of E and Q contains all the elements that are in E, which is the set of even numbers in the integers from 1 to 10.

(d) $P \cup Q = \{2, 3, 5, 7, 4, 8\}$

(e) $P \cap Q = \emptyset$

(f) $P \cap E' = \{3, 5, 7\}$

(g) $P' \cap E' \cap Q' = P' \cap E' = \{1, 9\}$

3.

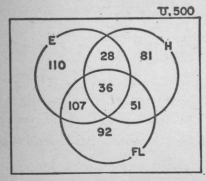

When we fill in the numbers, beginning at the center, our Venn diagram looks like this.

The numbers in the various areas add up to 505, and there are only 500 in the whole class.

*The Algebra of Sets

We pointed out earlier that union and intersection of sets are a bit like addition and multiplication of numbers in that they are commutative and associative. Let's investigate the other axioms that apply to numbers and see if there are other similarities.

Closure? Yes, for sets as for numbers. The union and intersection of two sets are themselves sets, as the sum and product of two rational or real numbers are themselves rational or real numbers.

Distributive law? Yes, but too many. There is only one distributive law for numbers, but two for sets (see pages 164–167).

Identities? There are numbers, 0 and 1, such that for every number, a,

$$a + 0 = a \quad \text{and} \quad a \times 1 = a$$

For sets, are there sets such that for every set A,

$$A \cup \boxed{?} = A \quad \text{and} \quad A \cap \boxed{?} = A$$

Certainly.

$$A \cup \emptyset = A \quad \text{and} \quad A \cap U = A$$

so that $\emptyset$, the empty set, acts like zero if the union symbol, $\cup$, corresponds to the plus sign, $+$. Also, U, the universal set, acts like 1 if the intersection symbol, $\cap$, corresponds to the multiplication sign, $\times$. What's more, for numbers,

$$a \times 0 = 0$$

and for sets

$$A \cap \emptyset = \emptyset$$

However, for sets

$$A \cup U = U$$

but for numbers $\quad a + 1 \neq 1$

Inverses? Is there something like a negative so that $A \cup \boxed{?} = \emptyset$ just as $a + (-a) = 0$? or like a reciprocal, so that $A \cap \boxed{?} = U$ just as $a \times \dfrac{1}{a} = 1$? No. We would expect A' to be some sort of inverse of A, but here the $\emptyset$ and U have to be interchanged to get true equations:

$$a + (-a) = 0 \quad \text{but} \quad A \cup A' = U \text{ (not } \emptyset)$$

$$a \times \frac{1}{a} = 1 \quad \text{but} \quad A \cap A' = \emptyset \text{ (not U)}$$

The first of these set equations says that *everything* is either in A or not in A. The second says that *nothing* is both in A and not in A.

Among the theorems that can be proved from the axioms for sets are these strange-looking ones:

$$A \cup A = A$$

$$A \cap A = A$$

These don't look much like facts in arithmetic where $a + a = 2a$, not a; and $a \times a = a^2$, not a. However, these equations say only that if something is in A *or* in A, it is in A, and that if something is in A *and* in A, it is in A.

Thus there is an algebra of sets which has some axioms in common with ordinary algebra, but which also has many differences.

Chapter 10
Mind Your p's and q's

The study of logic, the nature of valid reasoning, is an important part of mathematics. Here we define the exact meaning of the little words used to make new statements out of old: *and*, *or*, *not*, and *if*. The axioms about combining statements turn out to be very similar—*mutatis mutandis*—to those about operations with sets. We can design electric circuits to illustrate them.

Venn Diagrams in Logic

Johnny's mother said to him, "If you cross the street or if you climb a tree, you will get spanked." Later, Johnny got spanked. Which of the following is true?

(a) He crossed the street.
(b) He climbed a tree.
(c) He did both.
(d) He did one or the other.
(e) We can't tell what he did.

You might be surprised to learn that this question was on the mathematics part of a College Entrance Examination Board a few years ago. However, since mathematics involves proofs and since proofs involve combining statements properly so as to derive other statements, we need to study how to do this. This is the essence of deductive reasoning: starting with certain hypotheses and rules (that is, axioms) and deducing valid conclusions. Usually we are concerned with more weighty matters than the state of Johnny's posterior, but the substance of the illustrative example is unimportant (except to Johnny). Incidentally, the answer is (e), inasmuch as he may have committed some other spankable offense.

Venn diagrams are useful for deciding questions of this sort. In this case, if C is the set of occasions on which Johnny crossed the street, T the set of tree-climbing episodes, and S the set of occasions of spankings, then

$$C \subset S \quad \text{and} \quad T \subset S,$$

or

$$(C \cup T) \subset S$$

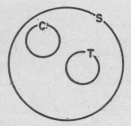

Sets C and T are non-overlapping (disjoint) sets, since the street-crossing episodes are considered to be distinct from the tree-climbing ones. If the tree were *across* the street, we might have pictured the sets as overlapping.

There is lots of room in S for episodes not in C or T, unfortunately for Johnny.

Basically, there are three kinds of Venn diagrams that fit the sorts of relations between two sets that occur as logical possibilities.

(1) All A is B, so $A \subset B$;
$A \cap B' = \emptyset$.
For example:
All ants are bugs.

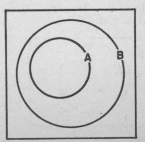

(2) No A is B, or all A is not B; $A \cap B = \emptyset$. For example: No apples are bananas.

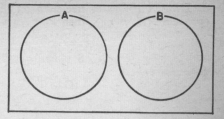

(3) Some A is B. For example: Some animals are bears.

(4) Some A is not B. For example: Some animals are not bears.

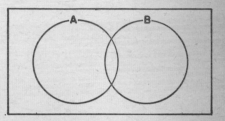

The last two statements, with the word *some*, are much weaker than the first two and do not exclude them. For instance, if "All ants are bugs," it is also true that "Some ants are bugs." If "No apples are bananas," it is also true that "Some apples are not bananas."

Let us consider these two arguments:

(1) All dogs are mammals.
   Spots is a dog.
   Therefore, Spots is a mammal.

(2) All dogs are mammals.
   Spots is a mammal.
   Therefore, Spots is a dog.

With the aid of the Venn diagrams, you should be able to see that the first of these two arguments is valid reasoning and the second is invalid.

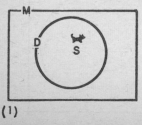

(1)

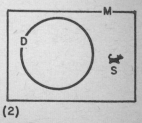

(2)

The trouble is that we might have drawn the second diagram incorrectly and made it the same as the first. We should have a better procedure than drawing Venn diagrams. If we are in doubt about the argument, we may be in doubt about the diagram, too. Later we will try to develop a more reliable procedure.

Note that we didn't say, in the second case, that Spots is not a dog, merely that he may not be. The conclusion was not valid but we made no statement about its truth.

(3) All dogs are bipeds.
All bipeds are human.
Therefore, all dogs are
human.

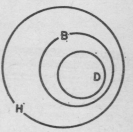

This argument is *valid*, although there is not a word of truth in any part of it, premises or conclusion.

(4) All dogs are bipeds.
All bipeds are mammals.
Therefore, all dogs are
mammals.

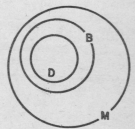

This is also a valid argument, even though it started with two false premises and ended up with a true conclusion. Truth and validity are quite different.

PROBLEMS

Are these valid arguments?

For example: Some animals are
bears.
Smokey is a bear.
Therefore, Smokey is an animal.

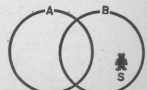

Not valid, as the Venn diagram shows, even though the conclusion is true.

The conclusion does not follow from the premises. We would need to replace the first with "All bears are animals" to make the argument a valid one.

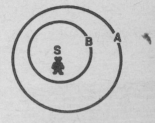

1. All Cretans are liars.
   Nick is a Cretan.
   Therefore, Nick is a liar.

2. All Cretans are liars.
   Nick is not a Cretan.
   Therefore, Nick is not a liar.

3. Some Cretans are liars.
   Nick is a Cretan.
   Therefore, Nick is a liar.

4. No Cretans are liars.
   Nick is a Cretan.
   Therefore, Nick is not a liar.

5. No Cretans are liars.
   Nick is not a Cretan.
   Therefore, Nick is a liar.

6. Some Cretans are liars.
   Nick is a Cretan.
   Therefore, Nick is not a liar.

ANSWERS AND EXPLANATIONS

1. Valid.

2. Not valid.

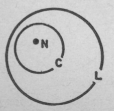

3. Not valid.   4. Valid.

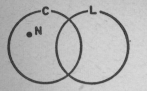   

5. Not valid.   6. Not valid.

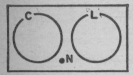   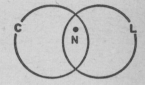

Combining Statements

Little words are often the most important. Logic assigns outstanding roles to *and*, *or*, *not*, and *if*. In the interest of brevity, it is conventional to use a single letter to stand for a whole statement. For example, *p* could mean "It is raining," or "Sugar is sour," or "Joe is a good dancer," or any other sentence, true or false.

"$p \wedge q$" means "*p* AND *q*." It is called the *conjunction* of the two statements.

"$p \vee q$" means "*p* OR *q*" (as usual, the word *or* includes the meaning "both"). It is called the *disjunction* of the two statements.

(Again, *verb. sap.* If you don't absorb the meanings of $\wedge$ and $\vee$, you will have trouble going on.)

If *p* = "Sue is pretty"   and   *q* = "Sue is quaint,"

then $p \wedge q$ = "Sue is pretty AND she is quaint"

and $p \vee q$ = "Sue is pretty OR she is quaint."

The analogy with union and intersection of sets is not hard to find. If P is the set of pretty girls and if Q is the set of quaint girls, the set diagrams are as shown below. Sue is in the shaded area.

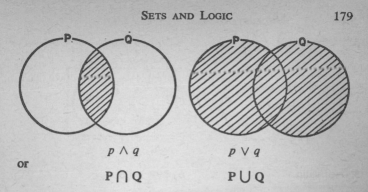

$$p \wedge q$$

or

$$P \cap Q$$

$$p \vee q$$

$$P \cup Q$$

To show exactly what $\wedge$ and $\vee$ mean, we use a *truth table*. There are four possible combinations of "true" and "false" for p and q. These are listed in the four rows of each table.

Conjunction

p	q	$p \wedge q$
T	T	T
T	F	F
F	T	F
F	F	F

Disjunction

p	q	$p \vee q$
T	T	T
T	F	T
F	T	T
F	F	F

The expression "$p \wedge q$" (p AND q) is true only when both p and q are true (the first row). The expression "$p \vee q$" (p OR q) is true for all cases except when both p and q are false (for the first three rows).

There is also a truth table, a very simple one, for negation. The symbol "$\sim p$" means "NOT p." While essentially this is an easy idea, using it may be hard.

p	$\sim p$
T	F
F	T

We can use truth tables to prove theorems about logic. For example, what is the negation of $p \wedge q$? If it is false that Sue is both pretty and quaint, what is she? You can probably see that she is either not pretty or not quaint, or neither. In symbols, this says

$$\sim(p \wedge q) \text{ is the same as } \sim p \vee \sim q$$

A theorem of this sort is called a *tautology*. (The word here has no denigrating overtones as it does in ordinary usage.) We can prove this by making a truth table for both expressions and seeing that they are the same. Here is the table:

1	2	3	4	5	6	7
p	q	$p \wedge q$	$\sim(p \wedge q)$	$\sim p$	$\sim q$	$\sim p \vee \sim q$
T	T	T	F	F	F	F
T	F	F	T	F	T	T
F	T	F	T	T	F	T
F	F	F	T	T	T	T

↑————same————↑

Columns 1 to 3 are the same as in our first table that defined "$p \wedge q$." Column 4 is the opposite of column 3 since column 4 is the negation of column 3. Column 5 is the opposite of column 1. Column 6 is the opposite of column 2. Column 7 is found by substituting from columns 5 and 6 in the definition of "$p \vee q$." Since columns 4 and 7 are the same, the two expressions, $\sim(p \wedge q)$ and $\sim p \vee \sim q$, are identical.

Here is another tautology:

$$\sim(p \vee q) \text{ is the same as } \sim p \wedge \sim q$$

This says that "It is false that Sue is either pretty or quaint" means the same as "Sue is not pretty and she is not quaint." Maybe this is obvious. Here is the proof:

p	q	$p \vee q$	$\sim(p \vee q)$	$\sim p$	$\sim q$	$\sim p \wedge \sim q$
T	T	T	F	F	F	F
T	F	T	F	F	T	F
F	T	T	F	T	F	F
F	F	F	T	T	T	T

↑————same————↑

The analogy with sets is again obvious.

$$(P \cap Q)' = P' \cup Q' \quad \text{and} \quad \sim(p \wedge q) = \sim p \vee \sim q$$
$$(P \cup Q)' = P' \cap Q' \quad \text{and} \quad \sim(p \vee q) = \sim p \wedge \sim q$$

These theorems are called De Morgan's Laws. They say, in effect, that the negation of an "and" sentence is an "or" sentence and vice versa.

PROBLEMS

1. Make the negation of these sentences:

(a) Roses are red and violets are blue.

(b) The suit will look good on you, or you can get your money back.

(c) It's hot and not humid today.

(d) He will buy her a mink coat, or she will not marry him.

*2. Use truth tables to prove both distributive laws. (Hint: We need 8 rows for the proof.)

(a) $p \vee (q \wedge r)$ is the same as $(p \vee q) \wedge (p \vee r)$

(b) $p \wedge (q \vee r)$ is the same as $(p \wedge q) \vee (p \wedge r)$

Make up an illustrative example for each.

3. Make the negation of each of these statements:

(a) All cats are black. (Be careful. It is NOT "*no* cats are black.")

(b) Some men are liars.

(c) No boys are polite.

(d) Some girls are not studious.

*(e) All July days are hot and some are humid.

*(f) No girls play football and some don't play baseball.

*(g) All knowledge is useful, or some books are not worth reading.

Answers and Explanations

1. In each case we can negate the sentence by putting "It is false that" in front of it. However, we can do a little better, using De Morgan's Laws.

(a) Roses are not red OR violets are not blue.

(b) The suit will not look good on you AND you can't get your money back.

(c) It's not hot OR it is humid today.

(d) He won't buy her a mink coat AND she will marry him.

*2. (a)

1	2	3	4	5	6	7	8
p	q	r	$q \wedge r$	$p \vee (q \wedge r)$	$p \vee q$	$p \vee r$	$(p \vee q) \wedge (p \vee r)$
T	T	T	T	T	T	T	T
T	T	F	T	T	T	T	T
T	F	T	F	T	T	T	T
T	F	F	F	T	T	T	T
F	T	T	T	T	T	T	T
F	T	F	F	F	T	F	F
F	F	T	F	F	F	T	F
F	F	F	F	F	F	F	F

↑————— same —————↑

(b)

1	2	3	4	5	6	7	8
p	q	r	$q \vee r$	$p \wedge (q \vee r)$	$p \wedge q$	$p \wedge r$	$(p \wedge q) \vee (p \wedge r)$
T	T	T	T	T	T	T	T
T	T	F	T	T	T	F	T
T	F	T	T	T	F	T	T
T	F	F	F	F	F	F	F
F	T	T	T	F	F	F	F
F	T	F	T	F	F	F	F
F	F	T	T	F	F	F	F
F	F	F	F	F	F	F	F

↑————— same ————↑

Illustrations:

Suppose p stands for "Bob is polite."

q stands for "Bob is quiet."

r stands for "Bob is rich."

(a) "Bob is polite OR he is quiet and rich" (column 5) means the same as "Bob is polite or quiet AND he is polite or rich" (column 8).

(b) "Bob is polite AND he is quiet or rich" (column 5) means the same as "Bob is polite and quiet OR he is polite and rich" (column 8).

If you think about these a while, they become clear even in words. The symbols are certainly clearer.

3. (a) Not all cats are black (this is *not* the same as "All cats are not black") OR some cats are not black.
   (b) All men tell the truth
       OR no men are liars.
   (c) Some boys are polite.
   (d) All girls are studious.
   *(e) Some July days are not hot OR none are humid.
   *(f) Some girls play football OR all play baseball.
   *(g) Some knowledge is not useful AND al books are worth reading.

Implication

We've left out so far the most interesting of the little words, "*if.*" The expression "$p \rightarrow q$" means "p IMPLIES q," or "If p is true, q is true," or more briefly, "If p, then q." This expression

"$p \rightarrow q$" does not mean that p causes q. There may be no logical connection between them at all, except that whenever p is true, q must also be true. Here is the truth table that defines implication.

p	q	$p \rightarrow q$
T	T	T
T	F	F
F	T	T
F	F	T

Probably, most people agree with the first, second, and last rows, and object violently to the third. However, the table *defines* the meaning of "$p \rightarrow q$," and there's no arguing with a definition. This particular definition is taken because it turns out to be useful. Let's see exactly what it means.

Row 1: Let p stand for "$2 + 5 = 7$"
and q stand for "The day after Thursday is Friday."

Then "$p \rightarrow q$" means "If $2 + 5 = 7$, then the day after Thursday is Friday."

This is certainly true. However, it does *not* say that p causes q. It says merely that whenever p is true, q is also true.

Row 2: Let p stand for "$2 + 5 = 7$"
and q stand for "The day after Tuesday is Friday."

Then "$p \rightarrow q$" means "If $2 + 5 = 7$, then the day after Tuesday is Friday." Although p is true, q obviously is false. Therefore $p \rightarrow q$ is false.

Row 4: Let p stand for "$2 = 5$"
and q stand for "$6 = 9$."

Then "$p \rightarrow q$" means "If $2 = 5$, then $6 = 9$." This is so. Note that in this case, we can derive "$6 = 9$" by adding 4 to both sides of "$2 = 5$." Of course, both are obviously false.

Even if we could not derive the q (the false conclusion) from p (the false premise), p would still imply q. For example, if p means "$2 = 5$" again and if q is changed to mean "$6 = 10$," $p \rightarrow q$ is still true. Since 2 does not equal 5, it makes no difference what the conclusion is.

Now for *Row 3:*

> Let *p* stand for "The moon is made of green cheese" and *q* stand for "$3 + 1 = 4$."

> Then "$p \rightarrow q$" means "If the moon is made of green cheese, then $3 + 1 = 4$." This is true, since $3 + 1 = 4$ regardless of the composition of the moon.

Another example, with a double-barreled statement for *p*:

> Let *p* stand for "$2 + 3 = 7$ *and* $13 + 16 = 27$" and *q* stand for "$15 + 19 = 34$"

> Then "$p \rightarrow q$" means "If $2 + 3 = 7$ and $13 + 16 = 27$, then $15 + 19 = 34$." This is true. In fact, we can derive "$15 + 19 = 34$" from the previous statement:

$$
\begin{array}{l}
2 + 3 = 7 \\
\text{Adding,} \quad 13 + 16 = 27 \\
\hline
\text{we get} \quad 15 + 19 = 34
\end{array}
$$

We had another example on page 176, where *p* stands for "All dogs are bipeds AND all bipeds are mammals," and *q* stands for "All dogs are mammals."

To summarize, "$p \rightarrow q$" is true except when *p* is true and *q* is false. A false hypothesis, *p*, implies any conclusion, *q*, true or false.

If $p \rightarrow q$, does $q \rightarrow p$?
> does $\sim p \rightarrow \sim q$?
> does $\sim q \rightarrow \sim p$?

We can answer these questions in at least three ways: by an illustration, by Venn diagrams, and by truth tables.

To use an illustration, let *p* stand for "Jane lives in Alaska" and let *q* stand for "Jane lives in the United States."

(1) Then "$p \rightarrow q$" means "If Jane lives in Alaska, she lives in the United States." True.

(2) Then "$q \rightarrow p$" means "If Jane lives in the United States, she lives in Alaska." False (that is, it is not necessarily true).

(3) Then "$\sim p \rightarrow \sim q$" means "If Jane doesn't live in Alaska, she doesn't live in the United States." False.

(4) Then "$\sim q \rightarrow \sim p$" means "If Jane doesn't live in the United States, she doesn't live in Alaska." True.

Using Venn diagrams, we need to think in terms of sets. Suppose P is the set of events or cases for which statement p is true. This is called the *truth set* of p. Similarly, Q will be the truth set of q.

$p \rightarrow q$ can be represented by:

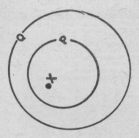

Anything in P is also in Q. In other words, any time p is true, so is q. Therefore, $P \subset Q$.

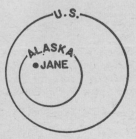

The United States corresponds to set Q, Alaska to set P, and Jane to X.

$q \rightarrow p$ is false since there can be elements in Q not in P; X is one not in P. $\sim p \rightarrow \sim q$ is false for the same reason: an element outside of P need not be outside of Q. (See figure on next page.)

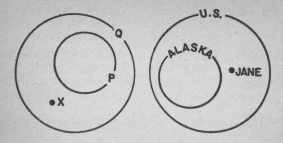

$\sim q \rightarrow \sim p$ is true, since any element not in Q cannot be in P.

Here is the truth table for the four implications we have been looking at:

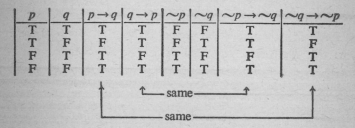

p	q	$p \rightarrow q$	$q \rightarrow p$	$\sim p$	$\sim q$	$\sim p \rightarrow \sim q$	$\sim q \rightarrow \sim p$
T	T	T	T	F	F	T	T
T	F	F	T	F	T	T	F
F	T	T	F	T	F	F	T
F	F	T	T	T	T	T	T

Therefore, not only is $p \rightarrow q$ equivalent to $\sim q \rightarrow \sim p$ but also $q \rightarrow p$ is equivalent to $\sim p \rightarrow \sim q$.

These four statements have names:

> If $p \rightarrow q$ is the *direct statement*,
> then $q \rightarrow p$ is its *converse*,
> and $\sim p \rightarrow \sim q$ is its *inverse*,
> and $\sim q \rightarrow \sim p$ is its *contrapositive*.

Thus, a converse has the "if" in the other clause, an inverse negates both clauses, and a contrapositive does both—has an "if" in the other clause and negates both clauses. If a statement is true, its contrapositive is true. Both its converse and inverse may be false; if one is false, so is the other.

Using the converse of a statement as if it meant the same thing as the direct statement is frequently the source of bad reasoning. For instance,

Direct Statement: If the Democrats are the majority party in Congress, conservatives will be chairmen of many powerful committees. (True)

Converse: If conservatives are chairmen of many powerful committees, the Democrats are the majority party in Congress. (False. Notice that *false* means that a statement is not necessarily true, not that it must be untrue.)

The technique of "guilt by association" usually depends on using a converse.

Direct statement: If Mike is a Communist, he thinks that Red China should be admitted to the United Nations. (True)

Converse: If Mike thinks that Red China should be admitted to the United Nations, he is a Communist. (False; that is, the statement is not necessarily true.)

Implications can be stated without the word *if*. For instance,

"If a person is an Alaskan, he is an American"

can be stated more simply as

"An Alaskan is an American." (True)

Its converse is

"An American is an Alaskan." (False)

Its inverse is

"A non-Alaskan is not an American." (False)

Its contrapositive is

"A non-American is not an Alaskan." (True)

PROBLEMS

1. Form the converse, inverse, and contrapositive of each of these true direct statements. Which converses and inverses are true? (The contrapositives *must* be true.)
   (a) I breathe if I sleep.
   (b) If a student fails to hand in homework, he won't get a good grade.
   (c) If $13x - 6 = 20$, then $x = 2$.
   (d) If I need something, I buy it.
   (e) Men are bipeds.
   (f) The American flag is red, white, and blue.

*(g) If $6y^2 - 15 = 39$, then $|y| > 2$.

(h) A rational number can be expressed as a repeating decimal. (See Chapter 7, pages 101, 102.)

2. What conclusions, if any, can you draw from these facts:
   (a) We won't go to the Fair if it rains. It did not rain.
   (b) Policemen must be 5′4″ or over. Bob is 5′3″ and Joe is 5′5″.
   (c) The cheerleaders are cute. Susie is a cheerleader.
   (d) The cheerleaders are cute. Mary is cute.

3. Is → commutative?

*4. Use a truth table to show that $p \to q$ and $\sim p \lor q$ mean the same thing. Make up an illustration.

ANSWERS AND EXPLANATIONS

1. (a) Converse: I sleep if I breathe.   ⎫
      Inverse: I don't breathe if I don't sleep. ⎬ False
      Contrapositive: I don't sleep if I don't breathe. ⎭

   (b) Converse: If a student gets a poor grade,   ⎫
                         he failed to hand in homework.   ⎪
      Inverse: If a student hands in homework,   ⎬ False
                         he will get a good grade.   ⎪
      Contrapositive: If a student gets a good grade, he ⎭
                         handed in homework.

   (c) Converse: If $x = 2$, then $13x - 6 = 20$. ⎫
      Inverse: If $13x - 6 \neq 20$, then $x \neq 2$. ⎬ True
      Contrapositive: If $x \neq 2$, then $13x - 6 \neq 20$. ⎭

   (d) Converse: If I buy something, I need it.   ⎫
      Inverse: If I don't need something, I don't ⎬ False
                         buy it.   ⎪
      Contrapositive: If I don't buy something, I don't need it. ⎭

   (e) Converse: Bipeds are men.   ⎫
      Inverse: Non-humans are not bipeds.   ⎬ False (for
                                                            ⎪ example,
      Contrapositive: Creatures that aren't bipeds aren't men. ⎭ birds)

   (f) Converse: A red, white, and blue flag is the ⎫
                         American flag.   ⎪
      Inverse: A flag that is not the American   ⎬ False
                         flag is not red, white, and blue. ⎭
      Contrapositive: A flag that is not red, white, and blue is
                         not the American flag.

*(g) First, solving the equation:

$$6y^2 - 15 = 39$$
$$6y^2 = 54$$
$$y^2 = 9$$
$$y = 3 \text{ or } -3, \text{ so } |y| > 2$$

Converse: If $|y| > 2$, then } False; numbers other
                 $6y^2 - 15 = 39$.   } than 3 and -3 have
Inverse: If $6y^2 - 15 \neq 39$, } absolute values great-
                 then $|y| \leq 2$.   } er than 2.
Contrapositive: If $|y| \leq 2$, then $6y^2 - 15 \neq 39$.

(h) Converse: A repeating decimal is a rational }
                 number.   } True
    Inverse: An irrational number cannot be   }
                 expressed as a repeating decimal. }

Contrapositive: A non-repeating decimal is irrational.
NOTE that, if the direct statements are accepted as true, all the
contrapositives are true.

2. (a) We can come to no conclusion. (To say that we went
       would be asserting the inverse.)

   (b) Bob is not a policeman; we don't know about Joe.
       If a man is a policeman, he is 5′4″ or over. Our conclu-
       sion about Bob uses the contrapositive. Any conclu-
       sion about Joe would use the converse.

   (c) } Susie is cute. If a girl is a cheerleader, she is cute.
and (d) } The direct statement applies to Susie. We make no con-
         clusion about Mary. To say that Mary is a cheerleader
         would be asserting the converse.

3. Definitely not. "$p \rightarrow q$" and "$q \rightarrow p$" are very different. The
   second is the converse of the first, and the converse can be
   false when the first is true.

*4.

p	q	$p \rightarrow q$	$\sim p$	$\sim p \vee q$
T	T	T	F	T
T	F	F	F	F
F	T	T	T	T
F	F	T	T	T

↑——— same ———↑

This tautology says that "Either p is false or q is true" means
the same as "If p is true, then q is true." Let the words sink in.

Any statement is either false or true, so we might amplify this into: "Either p is false or it is true, and in this case q is also true. So if p is true, then q is true." Again, the symbols are easier to handle than the words. An illustration might be: Suppose a clothing store advertises that if the suit you select doesn't fit, they will alter it. This statement can be amplified to say "Either the suit fits or it doesn't, in which case we will alter it." Now if

p stands for "The suit doesn't fit you"
q stands for "We will alter it."
"$p \rightarrow q$" means "If the suit doesn't fit you, then we will alter it."
"$\sim p \vee q$" means "Either the suit fits you, OR we will alter it."
These two sentences have the same meaning.

What Does "Only If" Mean?

(This section is hard. It must be taken slowly and carefully.)

(1) If it snows, the train is late.

(2) The train is late if it snows.

(3) The train is late only if it snows.

Do any or all of these mean the same thing? The first two do. The hypothesis, the *if*-clause, p, in both is "if it snows." It is a matter of style, not logic, if it comes at the beginning of the sentence or not. The third, however, is quite different. "The train is late only if it snows" means that snow is the only thing that makes the train late; in other words, "If it does not snow, the train is not late." This is the inverse of the other two sentences and may be false even if the others are true. Many things besides snow can make trains late.

Here is another example:

(1) Ann will pass the course if she gets over 90 on the exam.

(2) Ann will pass the course only if she gets over 90 on the exam.

The first is true, the second probably not. The second means the same as "If Ann does not get over 90 on the exam, she will not pass the course," an unlikely state of affairs.

To summarize:

Direct: $p \rightarrow q$.	Converse: $q \rightarrow p$.
If p, then q.	If q, then p.
q if p.	p if q.
p only if q.	q only if p.
p implies q.	q implies p.
Contrapositive: $\sim q \rightarrow \sim p$.	Inverse: $\sim p \rightarrow \sim q$.
If q is false, p is false.	If p is false, q is false.
q is false only if p is false	p is false only if q is false.

All the statements in the left column mean the same thing, and all those in the right mean the same thing, but the two columns are different.

Sometimes $p \rightarrow q$ AND $q \rightarrow p$.

Then

$$p \text{ if } q \text{ and } p \text{ only if } q,$$

$$q \text{ if } p \text{ and } q \text{ only if } p$$

are all true. We write this

$$p \leftrightarrow q$$

and say "p and q are equivalent."
Here is the truth table:

p	q	$p \leftrightarrow q$
T	T	T
T	F	F
F	T	F
F	F	T

For instance, 100 means "one hundred" if and only if we are using ten as a base.

$1 + 1 = 10$ if and only if we are using the binary system.

$1 + 1 = 0$ if and only if we are using the mod 2 system.

Sets A and B are disjoint if and only if A $\bigcap$ B $= \emptyset$.

$$y^2 = x^2 \leftrightarrow y = x \quad \text{or} \quad y = -x$$

$$x = 5 \leftrightarrow 2x = 10$$

$$(\sim p \vee q) \leftrightarrow (p \rightarrow q)$$

(See Problem 4, pages 188, 189.)

The phrase *if and only if* comes in so often that sometimes it is abbreviated *iff*. The first time I saw this, I thought it was a misprint, but it is just another instance of the mathematician's passion for compactness.

*PROBLEMS

You must be a citizen in order to vote. Which of these statements are true?

1. A person votes if he is a citizen.

2. A person votes only if he is a citizen.

3. If a person does not vote, he is not a citizen.

4. All voters are citizens.

5. If a person is not a citizen, he does not vote.

6. Either Mr. A did not vote, or he is a citizen.

7. A person is a citizen only if he votes.

8. A person does not vote only if he is not a citizen.

ANSWERS AND EXPLANATIONS

If "He votes" is p and if "He is a citizen" is q, we are told $p \rightarrow q$ (the direct statement).

1. False. This is $q \rightarrow p$, the converse.

2. True. This is p only if q, or $\sim q \rightarrow \sim p$, the contrapositive.

3. False. This is $\sim p \rightarrow \sim q$, the inverse.

4. True. This is the direct statement in other words.

5. True. This is $\sim q \rightarrow \sim p$, the contrapositive.

6. True. Either Mr. A did not vote or he did vote, in which case he must be a citizen. This is $\sim p \vee q$, which is the same as $p \rightarrow q$.

7. False. This is q only if p, or $\sim p \rightarrow \sim q$, the inverse.

8. False. This is $\sim p$ only if $\sim q$, or $q \rightarrow p$, the converse.

Direct and Indirect Proof

> "If it rains on Saturday, Jim goes to the movies.
> Last Saturday it was raining. Therefore, Jim
> went to the movies."

This is a simple, direct proof, $p \rightarrow q$ and p is true, so q must be true.

> p here is "It rained on Saturday."
>
> q here is "Jim went to the movies."

Compare that deduction with this one:

> "It can't have rained Saturday because if it
> had, Jim would have gone to the movies,
> but he didn't. He played baseball instead."

Here, using the same p and q, the argument is quite different.

$p \rightarrow q$ and q is false, so p must be false.

In fact, we are using the contrapositive here:

$$p \rightarrow q, \text{ so } \sim q \rightarrow \sim p$$

This sort of reasoning is called an *indirect proof*. It is used very frequently. To prove something by this method, we suppose that it is *not* true and see what can be deduced from this assumption. If what follows is impossible because it contradicts something known to be true, then our supposition must be false and its negation (what we wanted to prove) therefore must be true.

See if you can find that pattern here: "This salad must be made with pork or veal, not turkey, because it all looks like white meat."

> p here means "It is turkey salad."
>
> q here means "It has some dark meat."
>
> $p \rightarrow q$, and q is false. Therefore, p is false.
>
> So $\sim q \rightarrow \sim p$.

PROBLEMS

Analyze these arguments in the same way:

1. Joe must have thought this course was easy. He wouldn't have taken it if he'd thought it was hard.

2. The fuse must have blown because the light doesn't work, and I just tested the bulb and it's all right.

ANSWERS AND EXPLANATIONS

1. p is "Joe thought the course hard."
   q is "Joe would not take it."
   $p \to q$, but q is false (he did take the course), so p is false.
   Thus $\sim q \to \sim p$.

2. p is "The fuse is O.K."
   q is "Either the light works, or the bulb is broken."
   $p \to q$ and q is false since the light does not work *and* the bulb
   is good. Therefore, p is false.

In an argument like this we have to be sure about q. In actuality, this particular argument is very bad because there are other possible causes for a light's not working besides the fuse and the bulb. The switch, for instance, or the wiring might not be functioning. In an indirect proof, we eliminate one possibility and conclude the other holds. We must be sure, however, that there are only two or, if there are more, that we eliminate *all* except one.

*Boolean Algebra

Suppose we take our truth tables for disjunction, $\vee$, and conjunction, $\wedge$ (page 179), and rewrite them in the form usually used for addition and multiplication tables.

Disjunction, $p \vee q$ Conjunction, $p \wedge q$

$\vee$	F	T
F	F	T
T	T	T

$\wedge$	F	T
F	F	F
T	F	T

These say nothing new. The first says that $p \vee q$ is false only when both p and q are false; otherwise, $p \vee q$ is true. The second says that $p \wedge q$ is true only when both parts are true; otherwise, $p \wedge q$ is false. These look so much like arithmetic tables that it is tempting to go one step further and put numbers and arithmetic signs in them. Let us replace $\vee$ by $+$, $\wedge$ by $\times$, F by 0, and T by 1. Now the tables look like this:

$+$	0	1
0	0	1
1	1	1

$\times$	0	1
0	0	0
1	0	1

We have seen very similar tables before—when we were looking at the binary system, which has 2 as the base, and at the modular system with 2 as the modulus. Here are these tables again:

Base 2

+	0	1
0	0	1
1	1	10

×	0	1
0	0	0
1	0	1

Mod 2

+	0	1
0	0	1
1	1	0

×	0	1
0	0	0
1	0	1

For comparison, here is a small part of our ordinary arithmetic.

+	0	1
0	0	1
1	1	2

×	0	1
0	0	0
1	0	1

The four multiplication tables and three of the four sums in the four addition tables are identical. The only differences are $1 + 1$.

Ordinary arithmetic: $1 + 1 = 2$

Base two: $1 + 1 = 10$ (In base two, "10" means two)

Mod 2 $1 + 1 = 0$ ("0" is equivalent to two)

Logic: $1 + 1 = 1$ (*True* OR *true* means true)

The latter, addition in logic, just means that if p is true and q is true, then $p \lor q$ is true.

A set of axioms fitting the new set of tables has been worked out. It gives us a different sort of algebra suitable for operations with sets and with statements. It is called a *Boolean algebra* after George Boole (1815–1864) who first developed it in his "Investigation of the Laws of Thought." This algebra has only two numbers, 0 and 1, corresponding to false and true. (There are other Boolean algebras with more than two elements.) Some of its laws look very strange. For instance,

$$a + a = a \quad \text{and} \quad a \times a = a$$

$2a$ and a^2 couldn't be the answers as there is no "2" in this system.

a can be only either 0 or 1. You can check both these equations in the tables.

The algebra of statements and the algebra of sets are just the same, since everything we have said about statements has its counterpart in something about sets. Boolean algebra fits both. We can translate from one notation to another by using this "dictionary."

	Sets	Statements	Boolean algebra
	Capital letters, such as P, Q	Small letters, such as p, q	Small letters, such as a, b
basic ideas	$P \cup Q$	$p \vee q$	$a + b$
	$P \cap Q$	$p \wedge q$	$a \times b$
	P'	$\sim p$	$-a$
	$P \subset Q$ or $P' \cup Q = U$ or $P \cap Q' = \emptyset$	$p \to q$ or $\sim p \vee q$ is true or $p \wedge \sim q$ is false	$-a + b = 1$ or $a \times (-b) = 0$
	U	T	1
	$\emptyset$	F	0
a few equations	$P \cup P = P$	$p \vee p = p$	$a + a = a$
	$P \cap P = P$	$p \wedge p = p$	$a \times a = a$
	$P \cup P' = U$	$(p \vee \sim p)$ is true	$a + (-a) = 1$
	$P \cap P' = \emptyset$	$(p \wedge \sim p)$ is false	$a \times (-a) = 0$

Boolean algebra is suitable for solving logical problems, which is not surprising since it was devised just for that purpose. Such problems become exercises in computation, but the computation doesn't look much like our usual algebra and arithmetic, since the basic axioms are different. Computers can be designed to work out logical problems by having this algebra programmed into them. Its two numbers, 1 and 0, correspond to the two possible states of an electric circuit, current flowing or not, switch on or off, bulb lit or dark.

"It says the answer is 2."

You can build a very simple "computer" that will show $p \wedge q$ and $p \vee q$. For $p \wedge q$, there must be two switches *in series*, which means that current can flow only if both switches are closed. For $p \vee q$, we connect our two switches *in parallel*, which means that current can flow if either one or the other is closed.

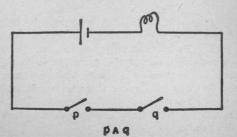

$p \wedge q$

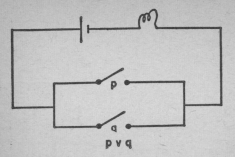

— ⊣|⊢ —   is the symbol for a battery or other source of current

— ⌿• —   is the symbol for a switch

— ෴ —   is the symbol for a light bulb

We can add another column to our "dictionary," one headed "circuits." A few items are

Sets	Statements	Boolean Algebra	Circuits
P $\cup$ Q	$p \vee q$	$a + b$	switches in parallel
P $\cap$ Q	$p \wedge q$	$a \times b$	switches in series
U	T	1	current flows
$\emptyset$	F	0	no current

Naturally the amount of Boolean algebra taught so far in schools is not enough to enable anyone to solve complicated logical problems with it—with or without computers. Most people who are not experts at it probably find truth tables easier to use than Boolean algebra, and Venn diagrams easier than either.

One way or another, we should all be able to think logically in mathematics and in daily life. Mathematics courses at all levels now stress the nature of proof and of logical reasoning. We hope the new knowledge is put to good use out of the classroom as well as in it.

Geometries: Euclidean, Non-Euclidean, and Others

Of all branches of human knowledge, geometry is probably the oldest one with a respectable history. Astronomy is as old, but many early ideas about the universe are no longer held to be true. In fact, in the Middle Ages, much of astronomy degenerated into astrology. Arithmetic developed early, but the lack of a suitable notation kept it from making much headway for long periods of time. The Greeks left some pronouncements about physics and anatomy, but they were largely incorrect. The weight of the authority of Aristotle and Galen, however, kept these sciences from progressing until comparatively late. Logic has an old and respectable history, but its study fell into relative obscurity until its reintroduction in the modern mathematics programs.

Geometry, on the other hand, was known and studied even before the golden age of Greece. The ancient Babylonians and Egyptians knew many geometric facts. Without these facts, the building and surveying that they did would have been impossible. However, the Greeks were more interested in the theoretical foundations of geometry than in its practical uses. There is a story that one of Euclid's pupils, after learning the first theorem, asked, "What advantage shall I get by learning these things?" Euclid replied by summoning a slave and saying "Give this fellow an obol* since he has to make a profit from what he learns." Ever since the Greeks, these two aspects of geometry, the pure, theoretical approach and the applied, practical point of view, have been intertwined in the study of geometry. In the modern mathematics courses, we tend to emphasize the former.

Geometry, as Euclid left it, came down from the Greeks almost without a break through the Middle Ages, when it was one of the

*A small Greek coin.

liberal arts in the quadrivium, to modern times. It is so much a part of our traditional education that cartoons like this appear without explanation in popular magazines. (The complicated

Drawing by Steinberg; © 1961 The New Yorker Magazine, Inc.

diagram in the balloon is essentially the one for Euclid's proof of the Pythagorean theorem. It has not changed through the centuries.) However, recently we have been examining the foundations of Euclid's geometry more carefully, attempting to understand its structure better and to eliminate some of its logical flaws (see Chapter 11).

If this time-hallowed subject is geometrY, what do we mean by geometrIES? What others can there be? Traditional geometry is a *metric* one. That is, measurements are meaningful, and lengths and angles do not change. Figures are rigid, and they can be moved around without changing their sizes or shapes. They exist in a space that we don't try to define or describe but that we feel fits our everyday experience. By changing some or all of these requirements, we can create other geometries.

The geometry that is useful in describing perspective drawings is not metric. Lengths and angles are not preserved when an object is photographed or drawn in perspective. This geometry is called *projective geometry*. Since it is not part of the modern school curriculum, it is not discussed in this book.

Another non-metric geometry is *topology* (see Chapter 12). There are geometries in spaces that don't conform to our ideas of common-sense reality. These may be non-Euclidean geometries (see Chapter 12) or geometries of more than three dimensions (see Chapter 13).

When we have glimpsed other geometries, we will be better able to see the place that our traditional geometry holds among them. It deals with special sorts of figures, those that can be moved rigidly, that can be transformed into others that differ in position but not in any essential attribute like size or shape. These figures are in a special sort of space. From a theoretical point of view, it cannot claim a pre-eminent place. In its practical, applied aspect, traditional geometry remains unique.

Chapter 11
Euclid Examined

We stress the axiomatic method. One way to do this is by considering miniature geometries with a small number of elements. Another way is by examining the omissions in the traditional set of axioms. These axioms can be supplemented by many others to obtain a more rigorous system.

Method in Mathematics

What is geometry? If you ever studied it in school, you probably remember it as a whole lot of facts about triangles, quadrilaterals, and other objects. These facts were to be proved and applied, and you spent a year doing this. Essentially, there are two aspects to geometry, its content and its traditional method. Here let us look at the method.

We begin with some undefined terms as we need a starting point, and we can't define everything. Suppose we don't know what the word *addition* means and try the dictionary. It says, "The process of combining two or more numbers so as to obtain their sum; denoted by a plus sign." We look up *sum* and find "the result of addition." We try *plus* and discover it means "indicating addition." Well, what have we learned? Precisely nothing. If we didn't know *addition* or *sum* or *plus* to begin with, we still don't. We have to have some words to build on, and we can't start with absolutely nothing.

After choosing our undefined terms and hoping everyone has a similar notion about them, we define some other words in terms of the undefined ones. Then we write down our rules for operating and call these *axioms* or *postulates*. Finally we prove statements called *theorems*, using all that has gone before.

In geometry, traditionally we take *line* and *point* as undefined. Then we define concepts like *angle* and *triangle*. Next we state axioms and postulates like "When equals are added to equals, the sums are equal" and "A straight line is the shortest distance between two points," and then we're off proving theorems and using them.

However, after reaching this point in our study of the new math, the description of the method used in geometry should sound very familiar—and not only because you may remember it from having had geometry in school. This is precisely the method we've been using all along in studying numbers, sets, and everything else we have mentioned. Our chief undefined terms were *natural number, addition, multiplication,* and *belongs to* or *is an element of.* Of course, there were others of less importance. We defined the other sorts of numbers (integers, rationals, reals) and other operations and relations (subtraction, division, intersection, and union). Then came the axioms and some proofs of theorems and their use in solving equations, working out logical problems, and various other applications. In other words, we used to think of deductive reasoning as being specifically the method used in geometry; now we realize that deductive reasoning pervades all mathematics. One famous definition of mathematics is that of Benjamin Peirce (1809–1880), "Mathematics is the science which draws necessary conclusions."

Once we have our definitions and axioms (or postulates), all of mathematics is contained therein. All the mathematician does is to draw all the conclusions he can find from them. From this point of view, all mathematics after the selection of the definitions and axioms is a tautology. It is an inevitable result. It is there all along, as an oak is in an acorn waiting to break out.

This means that it is extremely important to choose our axioms wisely. How is this done? What exactly is an axiom? The traditional answer: "An axiom is a self-evident truth." The modern answer: "An axiom is a statement to be used without proof." Possibly the most significant differences between the old and the new spirits in mathematics are those in these two sentences.

Nowadays, no one says an axiom must be self-evident, and no one says it must be true. In fact, like Pontius Pilate, we are not sure we know what truth is. All we ask from the axioms on this score is that they not contradict themselves or each other, for consistency replaces truth as our aim.

For example, an axiom in Boolean algebra (see page 195) is $a + a = a$. Is this self-evident? Not to most people. Of course, to a logician who has been working in this area it is obvious, but we could hardly require it to be self-evident before starting to use it. It is true? The question makes no sense. What is true is that a consistent algebra can be built using it.

Another example: the commutative law of multiplication, $ab = ba$. Most people would agree that this is both self-evident and true, but there are perfectly good algebras in which it is not possible. In the algebra of *quaternions*, invented by Sir William R. Hamilton (1805–1865) to apply to certain problems in mathematical physics,

$$ab = -ba$$

Quaternions are out of fashion now, but vectors, which have largely superseded them, share the same property of multiplication. For other objects called *matrices*, ab is not equal either to ba or to $-ba$ but is an entirely different quantity. Thus it is perfectly possible to get along without the commutative law for multiplication.

There are also non-associative algebras, in which the "self-evident truth" that $(ab)c = a(bc)$ is not so. No axiom is sacrosanct.

How then do we choose our axioms? The answer is, "Almost any way we like." The only restriction is that they must be consistent. It is also a good idea to have a fairly complete set, that is, enough of them to be able to build on.

How do we know if a set of axioms is consistent? If we have a system in which they do work without contradiction, they must be consistent. For example, the axioms for arithmetic and algebra work for the rational numbers, the real numbers, the complex numbers, the "clock-face" arithmetic with 5 as modulus, and many others. We have all these illustrations or models of this set of axioms. The axioms of Euclidean geometry seem to work for the physical world. We have that model to make us believe they are consistent. To prove a set of axioms consistent, we look for a model to which they apply.

To illustrate this idea, we can invent a miniature geometry with a few axioms and see if they work. Our miniature contains only a finite number of elements instead of the infinite number of points and lines in ordinary geometry. Here is an example of a *finite geometry*.

Undefined terms: *rudd*, *vory*

"A rudd *joins* two vories" means the same as "Two vories *are on* a rudd."

Axioms:

(1) There are exactly 4 rudds on each vory.

(2) There are exactly 2 vories on each rudd.

(3) Every vory is joined to every other vory by exactly 2 rudds.

Among the theorems that can be deduced is

There are exactly 6 rudds and 3 vories.

Is this a consistent set? If we can build a model to illustrate it, it is. Here are two such models.

(1) Think of a rudd as a curved line and a vory as a point.

(2) Think of a vory as a curved line and a rudd as a point.

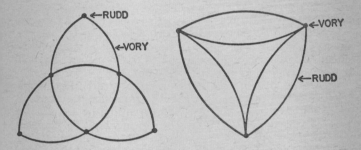

If you check the three axioms and the theorem in each diagram, you will find they work.

*PROBLEMS

Try to find models for this "geometry."

Undefined terms: *rask, syrl*

Axioms:

(1) Each syrl has exactly one rask in common with every other syrl.

(2) Each rask is on exactly two syrls.

(3) There are exactly four syrls.

Theorems that can be deduced include:

(1) There are exactly six rasks.

(2) Each syrl contains exactly three rasks.

(3) For each rask, there is exactly one other rask not on the same syrl.

Hint: You can use points and lines as syrls and rasks, in either order. If rasks are lines, your model must be in three dimensions. (Do you know the old puzzle about building four equilateral triangles, all the same size, with 6 matches, without breaking any matches? Most people can't do it because they think of everything in a plane, that is, on a flat surface.)

ANSWERS AND EXPLANATIONS

This must be done by experimenting with various configurations. If rasks are lines and syrls are points, the model is a

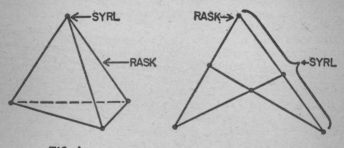

FIG. 1   FIG. 2

triangular pyramid, Fig. (1). If rasks are points and syrls are lines, our model is Fig. (2).

Suppose we tried deducing more theorems. Is there any guarantee that they will all work? This is a hard question to answer. In small systems like our finite geometries, there's not much that can be deduced, and no contradictions are likely to arise. In a larger set-up, however, like ordinary geometry, there are so many possible theorems that we can't foresee all of them. All we can say is that no incurable inconsistencies have yet appeared and that we think they probably won't.

Mathematicians would love to be able to prove that the sets of axioms they use are consistent and that no contradictions can ever arise. This hope motivated much research on the logical foundations of mathematics. However, in 1931, a young mathematician named Kurt Goedel proved that this ambition can never be realized: it is impossible to prove that a set of axioms for a system is consistent without going outside the system into a more complex one whose consistency is equally doubtful.

The axiomatic method thus has its limitations, but it has also had its brilliant successes. Euclidean geometry was one of them.

Euclid Improved

For many years "geometry" was "Euclid" and "Euclid" was "geometry." A student studying geometry was studying Euclid. There were a few minor variations: Changing the order in which certain theorems or constructions appeared made the work a little simpler. Better notation was invented here and there. By and large, a geometry textbook used to be fairly close to a translation from the original Greek of over two thousand years ago.

If that was good enough for two thousand years and up to a decade ago, why isn't it still?

The most valid answer is that Euclid's attempt to use the axiomatic method was faulty. That it was used at all as long ago as the time of the ancient Greeks is a tribute to their mathematical talents, but it was used imperfectly. Toward the end of the nineteenth century, it was noted by David Hilbert, Oswald Veblen, and other mathematicians that Euclid had not based his proofs solely on deductive reasoning from his axioms. He had made a strong appeal to intuition and he had used conclusions based on what was "obviously" true in diagrams. To take some simple examples, he used the fact that if two circles intersect, they do so twice. This seems *self-evident* (a word you

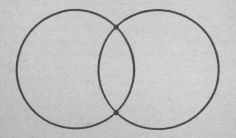

should now distrust), but it was nowhere stated as an axiom or proved as a theorem. He used the fact that a line cannot intersect one or three sides of a triangle. (If it intersects any side, it interesects two sides. It can, however, also intersect an extension of the third side.)

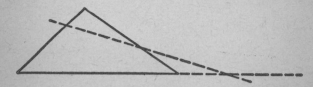

These tacit assumptions made it possible to "prove," by strict adherence to the axioms that were stated, several things that aren't so. One nice "proof" shows that a right angle is equal to another angle which is greater than a right angle. Another demonstrates that all triangles of whatever shape must have two sides equal. Such "proofs" are based on drawing diagrams in a plausible but actually impossible way—but a way not excluded by any of the axioms set down.

Another—less serious—blemish in Euclid is that some of the language is imprecise. This is less important and much more easily corrected than the imperfections in the axioms. Let us dispose of the chief differences in wording first and return later to the axioms.

(1) There should be a distinction made between a geometric object and a number that describes it in some way. We used to say "$RS = 3$ units," "angle $ABC = 45°$," "triangle XYZ is 2 square inches," and so on. What we meant was "The *length* of

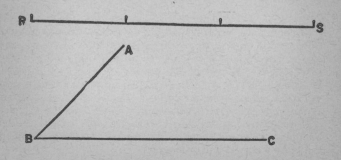

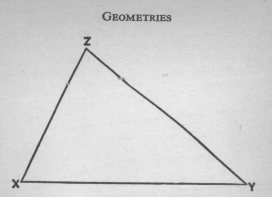

RS is 3 units," "the *size* of angle *ABC* is 45°," and "the *area* of triangle *XYZ* is 2 square inches." The word most commonly used now is *measure*. We talk about the measure of a line segment of an angle or of anything else in which a unit of measure is involved. Some books write "m(RS) = 2 units," "m($\angle ABC$) = 45°," and so on.

(2) The sign = and the word *equal* should mean that the two objects referred to are identical.

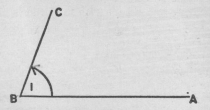

Thus, angle *ABC* might be called angle 1; so

$$\angle ABC = \angle 1$$

However, two different angles should not be called equal. The same applies to line segments. If their sizes, or measures, are the same, we can express this fact by saying that one can be placed on top of the other and they will coincide. The word for this is *congruent*, and its symbol is ≅ . This word used to be reserved for triangles that had the same size and shape, and occasionally we spoke about other congruent figures, like quadrilaterals or polygons. Now we have congruent angles and line segments.

It frequently was not clear if "triangle *ABC*" meant the lines bounding the shaded area or the shaded area itself. Similarly, is a circle a curved line or an area?

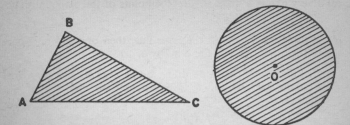

Now these definitions are given more exactly in set terminology:

(1) A line is a set of points.

(2) Line-segment *AB* is *A* and *B* and the set of points between them.

(3) Triangle *ABC* is the union of sets *AB*, *BC*, and *CA*.

(5) Circle *O* is the set of points a fixed distance from *O*.

Thus, triangles and circles are lines, not areas.

It should be noted that not all modern books agree on the importance of these distinctions; many ignore them, and some introduce other "new" vocabulary.

Correcting the set of axioms is a much more difficult task. There is no unanimity among textbook writers as to what the improved set of axioms should contain. Most textbooks follow Hilbert to some extent. However, he listed six groups of axioms (or postulates) about *connection*, *order* (or *betweenness*), *congruence*, *parallels*, *continuity*, and *completeness*—a total of twenty-one axioms—far too many, according to some people, to be inflicted on a high-school student. (Warning: most of the words describing the six groups have technical meanings.) Which of the twenty-one are most essential? This is largely a matter of taste. There is no agreement in geometry such as the agreement about the axioms for arithmetic and algebra.

Samples of the postulates used by various authors are:

(1) Every line contains at least two points.

(2) The points of a line can be placed in one-to-one correspondence with the real numbers.

(3) Every line in a plane divides the points of the plane into two sets.

(4) If three points are on the same line, then one and only one of them lies between the other two.

(5) If A and B are points on a line k and A' is a point on a line k', there are two points, B', on k', one on each side of A', such that

$$A'B' \cong AB$$

The sort of theorems proved from such axioms are statements like these:

(1) If P, Q, and R are on one line, and P, R, and S are on one line, then Q, R, and S are on one line.

(2) If A and B are on opposite sides of line k, then AB contains a point of k.

(3) If X and Y are both points inside angle O, then segment XY lies inside angle O.

Of course, if we are going to include these sorts of axioms and theorems, we shall have to omit some of the traditional material, or we shall need to spend an extra school year studying geometry. Unfortunately, there is not much agreement about what should be left out. However, the educators do agree that still more topics —some old and some new—should be put in.

There are three other additions to the traditional plane-geometry course which are desirable. One is a systematic study of logical processes, the nature of a proof—the sort of work we looked at in Chapter 10. Another is analytic geometry, that is, geometry on the Cartesian plane, studying points by using their co-ordinates and lines by considering their equations. The third is solid geometry, the geometry of three-dimensional space. The relations of lines and planes are as important as those of points and lines, and the properties of spheres as essential as those of circles.

With all this crammed in—logic, betweenness and other fundamental notions, analytic geometry, and solid geometry—a timesaving solution must be found. Some textbooks cut the traditional lists of theorems drastically, putting most of them in merely as exercises. Some integrate the analytic and synthetic (that is, traditional) geometry and save time besides by using analytic proofs, which in some cases are much easier. Some introduce a new axiom that makes it possible to rearrange the theorems and to simplify their proofs. Many textbook writers omit nothing and leave it to the teacher to decide what to leave out—if anything. One solution to the impasse is to teach more geometry on an intuitive basis in the earlier grades—elementary or junior high school—so that many of the properties of triangles, quadrilaterals, and circles are already known to the students by the time they reach high school. Then the regular high-school course in geometry can afford to spend more time on the new material. The content of the usual "new" geometry course is much more theoretical and more basic than that of a traditional course. One modern geometry textbook I have seen doesn't introduce the concept of congruent triangles until one-third of the way through the book. Older books usually brought them in almost at the beginning. In this newer book, the first third is taken up with logic and basic definitions and axioms about order, betweenness, and so on. Of course, the number of later theorems and exercises applying them is much reduced.

In general, this is true. Proofs of original exercises and numerical applications of geometry are now given less time and attention than formerly. If we go back to the Greek words that are put together to make the word *geometry* ("geo-" as in *geology*, *geography*, etc., and "-metry" as in *meter*, *thermometer*, etc.), we find it originally meant "earth-measurement." That is, geometry began as an aid to surveying. Today, nothing could be farther from the truth.

Chapter 12
Euclid Discarded

By changing one of Euclid's axioms, we can arrive at other consistent geometries. Topology can be very abstruse, but its simpler aspects are easy and fascinating. It is sometimes called *rubber-sheet geometry*. For example, if you draw a geometric figure on an elastic page and then distort it in any way, some properties do not change.

Non-Euclidean Geometries

There is one axiom, or postulate, that is included in every set used by every author, old or new, from Euclid through Hilbert to the writer of the latest textbook. This is the postulate (or supposition) about parallelism, which we have so far alluded to only briefly. (Parallel lines are lines in the same plane that never meet.) It says that through a specified point not on a straight line there can be exactly one line drawn parallel to the line. That is, through *P*, it is possible to draw one and only one line like

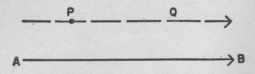

PQ which will be parallel to *AB*. (The arrowheads are the symbol for indicating parallel lines.)

This postulate has always seemed of a different nature than the others. Even when the others were considered self-evident, this one was not. Indeed, many people tried, unsuccessfully, to prove it.

One way to try to prove something is to suppose that it is not true and see what results. If what follows is impossible or contradicts something known to be true, then the supposition must be wrong. This is the essence of the indirect method of proof (see page 193).

In the case of the parallel postulate, there are two ways in which it might be false: (1) There might be more than one parallel, or (2) there might be no parallels. Both these suppositions contradict the statement that through a specified point not on a line there is exactly one line parallel to the line.

The case of two parallels attracted attention first. Saccheri (1667–1733) tried to prove that there is only one parallel by assuming that there are two and trying to show that the conclusions he could then draw were absurd. When he turned up no absurdities, he thought he had failed. Actually, he had laid the foundations of non-Euclidean geometry.

Later, Bolyai (1802–1860) and Lobachevsky (1793–1856) followed in his footsteps and constructed a consistent geometry based on the postulate that there are many lines through *P* that do not meet *AB*. Of course, the diagram looks wrong, that is, not convincing. But this can be expected, for, after all,

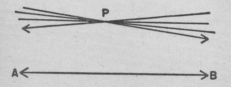

Euclid and his followers chose to assume only one parallel because that assumption seems to fit the physical world. One of the difficulties of studying non-Euclidean geometry is that the diagrams never look convincing and are rarely helpful.

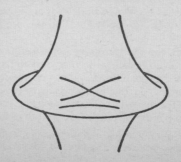

If we picture two trumpets placed with their large ends together, the surface formed, called a *pseudosphere*, is more suitable for Lobachevskian geometry than is a plane. Diagrams drawn on such a surface show two parallels to a "line"* through an outside point.

The other hypothesis, that there are *no* parallels, was developed by Riemann (1826–1866). This also leads to a consistent geometry, and is a little easier to imagine than the previous one. In a plane, we expect lines that form 90° angles with the same line to be parallel to each other, but on the curved surface of the earth, the meridians all make 90° angles with the equator and neverthe-

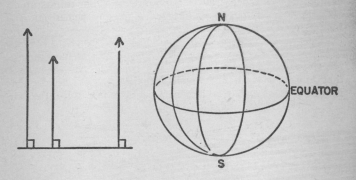

less meet at the north and south poles. This is what we expect in Riemannian geometry, where there are no parallels. The surface of a sphere is suitable for this geometry, as the surface of a pseudosphere is for the other non-Euclidean one. In the Einstein theory of relativity, space seems to be curved. Like the surface of a sphere, it is finite but unbounded—a concept impossible for most people to imagine. However, Riemannian geometry fits this idea, and it has been used in developing Einstein's theory of the universe. It is still an open question if space is Euclidean or non-Euclidean.

Some theorems are the same whether we assume one parallel, many parallels, or no parallel, but many are different. The most familiar of those that are different is the one about the sum of the angles of a triangle. In Euclidean geometry (one parallel), that sum is 180°. In the many-parallels geometry, it must be less than 180°. In the no-parallel geometry, it is always more than 180°.

*This is the nearest thing to a straight line on a plane. It is actually the shortest distance between two points on this surface.

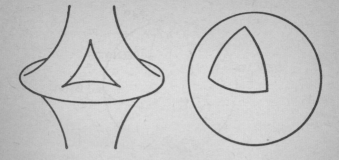

In the latter two, the amount by which the sum differs from 180°
depends on the size of the triangle. (Therefore, small triangles
on a sphere or on a pseudosphere appear very much like plane
triangles.)

Although non-Euclidean geometries are not studied in much
detail in schools, they must be mentioned if we want to stress the
importance of our choice of axioms and postulates.

PROBLEMS

1. If you laid out a triangle on a football field and measured the
   angles, what do you think you would find for their sum?
   What if you could use a very large triangle, for instance, one
   whose sides are the equator, the Greenwich meridian, and the
   meridian through New York City? (The meridians are the
   north-south "lines" passing through the poles. They are
   assigned a number according to the distance in degrees they
   are from a zero meridian. These degrees are called *degrees of
   longitude*. The longitude of New York City is about 74°
   west of Greenwich, England.)

2. Discuss Bertrand Russell's famous definition of mathematics
   as "the subject in which we never know what we are talking
   about, nor whether what we are saying is true."

ANSWERS AND EXPLANATIONS

1. In the first case, except for errors in measurement, you should
   get 180°. In the second case, the effects of the curvature become apparent; here the sum is 90° + 90° + 74°, or 254°.

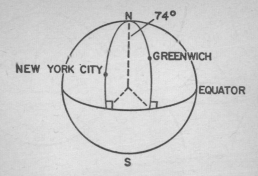

2. This sounds shocking—which was probably Lord Russell's motive when he said it—but there is considerable truth in it. It emphasizes the abstract nature of mathematics and the axiomatic method. We start with undefined terms, so in that sense we never know what we are talking about. We say that if one thing is true, then another is. Never do we assert positively that the first is true. All of mathematics is in the form of statements like "If p, then q," but we never say we know about p.

Topology: Geometry Without Size or Shape

One of the most important symbols in our usual geometry is $\cong$ meaning "congruent." The sign is made up of two parts, $=$ and $\sim$, standing for "equal" and "similar," referring to size and shape. Equal figures are the same size. Similar figures are the same shape. Congruent figures are the same size and shape. Every page in a geometry book bristles with one or more of these symbols and ideas. Can you imagine a geometry with none of them in it? What would be left?

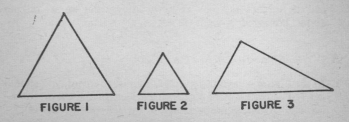

FIGURE 1   FIGURE 2   FIGURE 3

For example, let's start by thinking of a triangle, each side of which measures 1 inch (Figure 1). If we forget about the size, that is, forget about the 1 inch, we still have a triangle with all sides equal: this fixes its shape (Figure 2). Now forget that too. Make it any triangle (Figure 3). But the word *triangle* still specifies its shape, not as definitely as when we kept the sides equal, but still as being triangular. Forget that too. Then what can the figure be? It could be any of these in Figure 4. What do they have

FIGURE 4

in common with our original triangle? Well, at least they are more like it than the following:

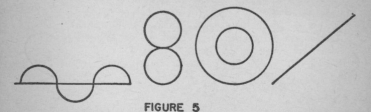

FIGURE 5

For one thing, if the triangle had been made out of an elastic band, it could have been deformed into any of the diagrams in Figure 4, but not into any in Figure 5. If it had been drawn on an infinitely stretchable sheet of rubber, the same would be true.

Topology has been called *rubber-sheet geometry*. It is the study of those properties that remain unchanged (*invariant* is the technical term) when a figure is stretched or twisted in any way without being torn.

A more formal statement about what all the diagrams in Figure 4 have in common with the original triangle and with each other is that all of them divide the plane into two parts, an inside and an outside. They are said to be *topologically equivalent*. In Figure 5, the first diagram has three insides and an outside, the second has two insides and an outside, the third has two outsides and an inside, and the last has no inside. (The third has two outsides

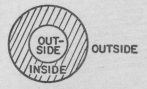

and an inside because it is thought of in this way.)

Suppose we start with a 2-inch straight-line segment *AB* with *C* as its midpoint. What is left of this if we change its size and

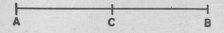

shape as much as we like? In other words, what are its topological equivalents?

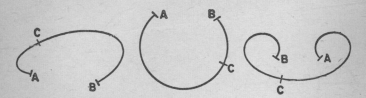

The lengths of *AB*, *AC*, and *CB* can all change, and the straightness is no more. What remains? That is, what are its topological *properties*? There are some: (1) It does not cross itself, (2) *A* and *B* each have points on only one side of them, and (3) *C* is between them.

The topological properties are in general among those ignored by Euclid and included in a modern course: for instance, the concepts of order, betweenness, interior and exterior, and so on.

Topology originated in the problem of the seven bridges of Koenigsberg. Koenigsberg lies on the Pregel River, which has two islands there. There were seven bridges, as shown in the diagram.

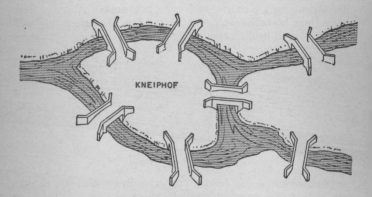

KNEIPHOF

The Sunday strollers used to try to walk so that they would cross each bridge exactly once. No one ever managed it, so they finally asked the mathematician Euler (1707–1783) to plan such a route. He proved it to be impossible. This is a topological problem, because the sizes and shapes of the islands and bridges are unimportant. In fact, Euler thought of the land masses as points (vertices), and of the bridges as lines, and replaced the map by

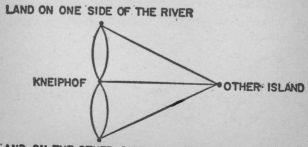

LAND ON ONE SIDE OF THE RIVER

KNEIPHOF

OTHER ISLAND

LAND ON THE OTHER SIDE OF THE RIVER

this diagram, called a *network*. In this form, it is fairly easy to see that, in order to traverse a network in one trip without going over any branch twice, there must be at each vertex an even number of branches, one leaving for every one arriving. The only exceptions can be at the beginning, where we leave without having arrived, and at the end, where we arrive without leaving. In other words, all but two of the vertices must be even, that is, must have an even number of branches converging there. In the Koenigsberg problem, all four vertices are odd: three of them have three branches each, and one has five. Therefore, the walk over all seven bridges cannot be made in one trip without going over one of them twice.

On the other hand, this network can be traversed, since all

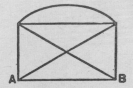

vertices except *A* and *B* have four branches, and *A* and *B* have three. Thus, we should start at *A* and end at *B*, or the other way around, and find such a path. Let's try it. There is more than one way to go. Remember, though, if we start at any other point, it can't be done.

If all the vertices are even, we can start anywhere, and we shall end where we started. If there are four odd vertices, the network can be traversed in two trips. If there are six vertices, in three trips; and so on. It is impossible to have a network with one, three, or any other odd number of odd vertices.

PROBLEMS

1. Which of these figures is not topologically equivalent to the others?

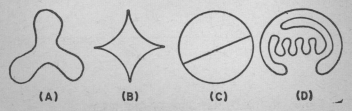

(A)   (B)   (C)   (D)

2. This curve is topologically equivalent to a circle. Is *P* inside or outside?

3. In three dimensions, we have the same sort of equivalence. If figures can be deformed into each other on the assumption that they are made of a perfectly stretchable, flexible material, then they are topologically equivalent.* For instance, a flat plate, a ball, and a water glass are all equivalent.

Which of these are equivalent: a cup with a handle, an inner tube, a soda straw, and a doughnut?

*Some equivalent figures cannot be deformed into each other unless they are cut, untwisted, and the cut edges then reattached. For instance, these two knots are equivalent to a circular loop and to each other.

4. Can these networks be traversed in a single trip? If so, find a route.

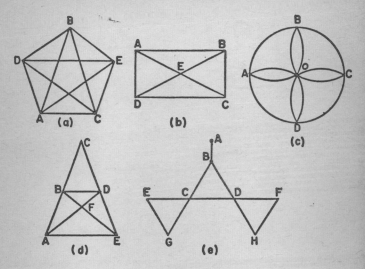

(a) (b) (c) (d) (e)

*5. Is it possible to walk through the apartment whose floor-plan is given here, passing through each door exactly once?

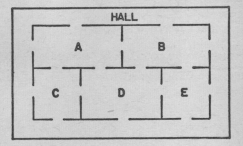

ANSWERS AND EXPLANATIONS

1. (c) is different. It has two interiors, whereas the others have one.

2. Inside. The shaded area is the interior of the figure.

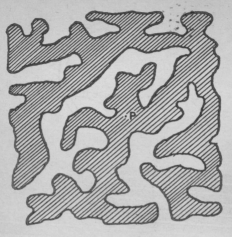

3. All are equivalent. All could be deformed into a ball with a hole through it.

4. (a), (c), (d), and (e) can be traversed in one trip. In (a), all the vertices are even, so we can start anywhere. One route is *ABCDEADBECA*.

In (b), *A*, *B*, *C*, and *D* are all odd, with three branches each. It can be traversed in two trips. *ABCDAC* could be one, and *BD* the other.

In (c), all the vertices are even, so we can start anywhere. One route is *AOCOABODOBCDA*.

In (d), *A* and *E* are odd, so the route must start at one and end at the other. One route is *ACEBDAE*.

In (e), *A* and *B* are odd. One route is *ABCGECDFHDB*.

*5. No. *A*, *B*, *D*, and the hall have an odd number of doors.

Topology deals with all sorts of configurations, from knots to maps to peculiar surfaces. Classifying knots is a difficult topological problem. Many magician's tricks are based on topological properties of knots. The three-ring sign has a surprising feature:

all three rings are connected, but no two are. Remove one and the other two are free.

How many colors are needed to color any map so that no two regions with a common boundary are colored alike? This is a real puzzler. No one has come up with a definite answer yet. Here is a map that needs four colors, so the answer is at least

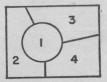

four. Topologists are inclined to think that four is enough for any map. At any rate, no one has ever constructed a map that needs more. It has been proved that five colors are always sufficient, but no one has proved that four are. If you want to become famous in the world of mathematics, solve the "four-color problem." That is, either make a map that requires five colors, or prove that four are always enough.

The most curious oddity of elementary topology is the surface with one side and one edge known as the *Moebius strip*. If you cut a long narrow strip of paper and paste its ends together to get something like a belt, of course it has two sides, inside and outside, and two edges, top and bottom. A bug crawling on the outside couldn't get to the inside without crossing an edge. This seems a natural and inevitable state of affairs (Figure 1).

Now suppose that, before pasting the ends together, we give one of them a half-twist; now we have a Moebius strip. A bug could crawl over all of it without crossing its one and only edge. If we apply paint all along one side, we've painted it all. I don't

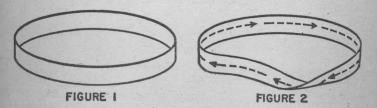

FIGURE 1   **FIGURE 2**

expect you to believe it unless you try it (Figure 2).

The Moebius strip has other interesting properties. Can you imagine what will happen if we cut it along a line down the center? Not many people can. An ordinary belt, made from an untwisted strip, cut in this way, would result in two belts, each half the width of the original. Here, we get one belt, half as wide and twice as long as the one with which we started.

If we give one end of the strip a whole twist before pasting the ends together, the resulting surface will have two sides and two edges. What if we cut this last strip down the center? Suppose we start with three half-twists? What if we start our cut of a Moebius strip (one half-twist) one-third of the way from the edge and keep that spacing all the way around? I won't answer these questions here. You'll enjoy it more if you find out the answers by trying it. However, if you want to check your results, look at the end of the chapter.

Here are two other oddities: The first is a Klein bottle (Figure 3),

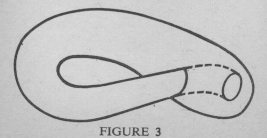

FIGURE 3

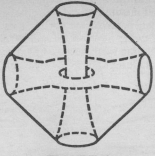

FIGURE 4

which is a bottle that has no inside—a sort of a three-dimensional Moebius strip. The second oddity is a hole through a hole in a hole (Figure 4).

Of course, topology is not just tricks and puzzles. Its theorems are proved by deductive reasoning, not by paste and scissors. It is the basis for advanced work in many fields of mathematics. However, this study gets quite difficult, and therefore is still reserved for college courses.

RESULTS OF CUTTING VARIOUS MOEBIUS STRIPS

A strip with	A cut	Gives
2 half-twists	down center	2 interlocking rings.
3 half-twists	down center	1 long knotted ring.
1 half-twist	1/3 of the way from its edge	2 interlocking rings: 1 long and 1 short.

What's It Worth?

Chapter 13
Is There More?

There are several other topics that have been suggested for inclusion in high-school courses and that are being used in some schools. Among them are *n*-dimensional geometry, groups, vectors, and matrices. Some traditional subjects are now taught with a different emphasis.

Other New Topics

In the preceding chapters, I have described the essentials of some of the new topics in school mathematics. Naturally, not all schools are teaching the same courses. There are probably very few, if any, whose choice of topics agrees completely with mine. Most teach some, but not all, of what is in this book. Some teach more, for there are many other subjects which are new, interesting, and suitable for high-school students. The trouble lies in finding the time to treat everything we would like.

Among the new topics studied in some schools and not discussed in the preceding chapters are:

(1) n-*dimensional geometry*. (We are already acquainted with plane geometry, which deals with two dimensions, and with solid geometry, which involves three dimensions.) One-dimensional geometry is restricted to configurations on a line, and therefore might not be very interesting or challenging to some of us. But what about four or more dimensions? If we take a point and move it 1 inch, we get a 1-inch line segment. If we move this line segment 1 inch in a direction perpendicular to itself, we get a 1-inch square. If we move the 1-inch square 1 inch in a direction perpendicular to itself, we get a 1-inch cube. What happens if we move the cube in a direction perpendicular to itself? Well, of

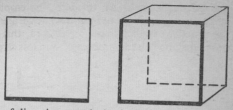

course, we've run out of directions, and physically we can't do it. However, we can *think* of doing it. The resulting figure is called a *tesseract* or *hypercube*.

We may also appreciate the following relationships:

A point has 1 vertex (itself).
A line segment has 2 vertices (its ends).
A square has 4 vertices (its corners).
A cube has 8 vertices (its corners).

A tesseract must have 16 vertices to continue the pattern. Does that help you picture it? Although no one can imagine objects in more than three spatial dimensions, it is possible to build up a geometry and develop theorems about them.

(2) *Groups.* This is a word that has a special mathematical meaning that does not resemble its ordinary one. A group is a set of elements with one operation. Sets of numbers ordinarily have two: addition and multiplication. The axioms for a group are closure, the associative law, and the existence of an identity and inverses. Some groups are also commutative. The elements in a group are not necessarily numbers. These elements are often rotations, substitutions, or other actions. The important thing is that a group has a structure that can be completely abstract and that can describe a number of different concrete things. The theory of groups has been used in many areas of mathematics—from the question of what sorts of equations can be solved to the rotations of a triangle and of a twenty-sided solid.

(3) *Vectors* and *matrices*. While these are not numbers in the ordinary sense, they can be added and multiplied. Multiplication, however, is not commutative. Matrices are useful in solving sets of simultaneous equations. When there are many equations and many unknowns, matrix methods turn out to be suitable for use in computers, which can thus solve such sets very quickly.

Other Changes

What about all the traditional mathematics courses? They are still with us, in name at least. The content has naturally not remained unchanged. All through, the emphasis is more on the structure and abstract nature of what we are studying and less on the practical applications. In algebra, this means fewer "word problems" or "puzzle problems" and less stress on computational

"If it takes John six and a half hours to paint the barn, and it takes Bill four and three-quarter hours to paint the barn, how long will it take John and Bill to paint the barn together?"

Drawing by Richter; Copyright © 1946 The New Yorker Magazine, Inc.

skill. In studying logarithms, for example, formerly we spent a lot of time on lengthy and involved calculations. Now, the idea seems to be that anyone who has to do such computations probably has access at least to a desk computer, if not to the largest IBM model. Therefore we do fewer long calculations and emphasize instead the nature and behavior of the logarithmic function.

In trigonometry, the same sort of thing is true. Etymologically, the word *trigonometry* means "triangle measurement." Traditionally we spent a lot of time and energy solving triangles, that is, finding the sides and angles we did not know from those we did. To do this, we used trigonometric functions among which were some called *sines*, *cosines*, and *tangents*. Now, we stress instead the functions themselves, their interrelationships and basic characters. When we used to speak of a sine, or of any other trigonometric function, it was always the sine of an angle; now, it can be the sine of a number. We are farther and farther from the idea of measuring triangles. Possibly the name *trigonometry* should be changed.

Advanced algebra courses have always included a section on probability and statistics. This topic has assumed more and more importance in new curricula, and, in some schools, a whole semester is now given over to it. If a student has had such a course, it should no longer be true for him that "you can prove anything by statistics." If 55 out of 100 voters polled are for candidate A, the student should know with how much confidence A's backers can predict victory. (Naturally, this depends on the total number of voters.) In tossing coins, we expect about the same number of heads and tails. If you toss a penny 100 times and get 55 heads, is the coin not a fair one or is getting 55 heads just chance? What if you get 550 heads in 1000 tosses?

We can't go into the theory of this here, but you may be interested in the answers. In the polling question, the reason the total number of voters is important is that it is very hard to choose a representative sample. A group of 100 might be a fair sample of 10,000 or so, but it is very unlikely to reflect accurately the views of a million. Otherwise, this question is very similar to the first one about the coin. In a set of only 100 tosses of a coin, a deviation of 5 one way or the other from the expected 50 heads is not very significant; it *is* suggestive, however, but far from being conclusive. However, if the trend continues, so that in 1000 tosses we get a deviation of 50 from the expected 500 heads, this is very unlikely to be merely chance. That is, the coin is probably not evenly balanced.

A new development in high school, although not new mathematics, is the teaching of analytic geometry and calculus on the college level. This is part of the Advanced Placement Program, in which many colleges accept work done in high school if it satisfies their standards. Even here, the new spirit appears. Calculus is now taught in a more abstract and rigorous fashion than it used to be. There is less stress on mechanics and more on its theoretical foundations than formerly.

Chapter 14
Conclusion

Mathematicians and mathematics teachers are not entirely in agreement about the value of the new courses. Here is an attempt to evaluate the programs and to indicate the directions in which further progress may be made.

Does *new* mean *better?* This question has been agitating mathematicians and mathematics teachers for the last few years, and controversy is sometimes heated. Mathematics has been called "the queen and servant of science" (a book by Eric T. Bell has that as its title). By and large, reactions to the new mathematics depend on whether you think the role of queen or that of servant is more important. Nevertheless, the queen's supporters are more pleased than the servant's with the new developments.

Those who think of mathematics primarily as a tool are not too happy at what they consider playing down computational techniques and concrete applications in favor of abstraction, theory, and rigor. The chief exponent of this view is Dr. Morris Kline of New York University. In an article in its *Alumni News* (October, 1961) and elsewhere in articles and speeches, he has charged that mathematics is being isolated from the physical and social sciences although its primary value is that it is their language and essential instrument. Now, it has become too abstract, and it serves only the purposes of professional mathematicians and logicians. The direction of reform has been almost wholly misguided. The purported improvements will undoubtedly result in far less successful teaching of mathematics and in injury to the mathematical and scientific development of our country.

The "queen-supporters," on the other hand, say that the old methods of drilling on mechanics never worked anyway and that many students finished high school unable to carry out a computation or to solve a simple problem in spite of having spent years on those types of exercises. The same people say that a new method stressing the "why" rather than the "how" could not have worse results and seems very likely to have better ones. Besides, most students will not be engineers or physicists, and the traditional course was mainly suited for them. The new material emphasizes the underlying nature of mathematics and of logical ways of thinking. Nothing can be more important than these aspects. The abstract approach is not too hard. The enthusiasm with which youngsters approach the new curriculum shows that it is not over their heads. The needs of the country, especially in the social sciences, can be met only by including many of the new topics.

If I may be permitted a personal opinion in conclusion, it is this: There was some dead wood and much that was and still is valuable in traditional mathematics courses. In the new ones, there is much that is stimulating and worthwhile, and some that is trivial—like proving obvious facts in algebra and in geometry in order to be rigorous. I hope it is not an "either-or" situation. Mathematics can be a tool for scientific work and at the same time an end in itself.

Mathematics teachers must now try to combine the best elements from the old and the new mathematics, bring mathematics up to date without losing the contributions of earlier thinkers, and use the creativity and curiosity of youngsters so as to increase their interest in mathematics. Mathematics classes can be stimulating and exciting. The new courses seem to help make them so.

Some New Words and Symbols

Collected and Simply Defined for Ready Reference

Laws

1. *Closure:* There is in the set one and only one resu't of the operation.

   The set of odd numbers is closed to multiplication, because the product of two odd numbers is odd. But the set of odd numbers is not closed to addition, because the sum of two odd numbers is even.

2. *Commutative Law:* One order is as good as the other.

$$3 + 5 = 5 + 3 \qquad 3 \times 5 = 5 \times 3$$

3. *Associative Law:* Group them any way you like.

$$2 + (3 + 4) = (2 + 3) + 4 \qquad 2 \times (3 \times 4) = (2 \times 3) \times 4$$

4. *Distributive Law:* Multiplication distributes itself over addition, because $a \times (b + c) = (a \times b) + (a \times c)$.

$$3 \times (4 + 7) = 3 \times 11 = 33$$

$$or \quad = (3 \times 4) + (3 \times 7) = 12 + 21 = 33$$

Names for Special Numbers

1. *Identity:* The number (or element) that doesn't change what it operates on.

   The identity for addition is zero. The identity for multiplication is 1.

2. *Inverse:* A number (or element) combined with its inverse gives the identity.

For addition, negatives are inverses, because

$$(-a) + a = 0$$

For multiplication, reciprocals are inverses, because

$$\left(\frac{1}{a}\right) \times a = 1$$

Symbols Used with Sets and Statements

1. $\cup$ The *union* of two sets is the set of everything in either or both of them. ($\cup$ should suggest Union.)

   $\vee$ The *disjunction* of two statements says that either or both of them is true. ($\vee$ equals OR.)

2. $\cap$ The *intersection* of two sets is the set of everything in both of them.

   $\wedge$ The *conjunction* of two statements says that both of them are true. ($\wedge$ equals AND. It should suggest "A" for AND.)

3. $\subset$ One set is a *subset* of a second if whatever is in the first is also in the second.

   $\rightarrow$ One statement *implies* a second if, whenever the first is true, the second is also true.

4. A' The *complement* of a set contains everything not in it.

   $\sim p$ The *negation* of a statement says that it is not true. ($\sim$ should suggest minus.)

5. $\emptyset$ The *empty set*, or the *null set*, is the set with no elements.

   U The *universe*, or the *universal set*, is the set of everything under consideration.

The Four Kinds of Implication

1. *Direct:* If p is true, then q is true.

2. *Converse:* If q is true, then p is true.

3. *Inverse:* If p is false, then q is false.

4. *Contrapositive:* If q is false, then p is false.

Suggestions for Further Reading

General works about mathematics, old and new, for the non-mathematician:

Bell, Eric T., *Mathematics: Queen and Servant of Science*. New York: McGraw-Hill Book Company, Inc. 1951.

Bell, Eric T., *Men of Mathematics*. New York: Simon and Schuster, Inc., 1937.

Bergamini, David, and the Editors of LIFE, *Mathematics*. Time Incorporated, 1963.

Courant, Richard, and Herbert Robbins, *What Is Mathematics?* New York: Oxford University Press, 1946.

Dantzig, Tobias, *Number: the Language of Science*. New York: The Macmillan Company, 1949.

Gamow, George, *One, Two, Three, Infinity*. New York: The Viking Press, Inc., 1947.

Kasner, Edward, and James Newman, *Mathematics and the Imagination*. New York: Simon and Schuster, Inc., 1940.

Kramer, Edna, *The Main Stream of Mathematics*. Greenwich, Conn.: Fawcett Publications, Inc., Premier Book T130

Lieber, Lillian R., *The Education of T. C. Mits*. W. W. Norton & Company, Inc., 1944.

Sawyer, W. W., *Prelude to Mathematics*. Baltimore, Md.: Penguin Books, Inc., 1955.

Works about modern mathematics in particular:

Adler, Irving, *The New Mathematics*. New York: The John Day Company, Inc., 1959.

Adler, Irving, *Thinking Machines: A Layman's Introduction to Logic, Boolean Algebra and Computers*. New York: The John Day Company, Inc., 1961.

Aiken, Desmond, and Charles Beseman, *Modern Mathematics: Topics and Problems* (pamphlet). McGraw-Hill Publishing Company, Inc., 1959.

Brant, Vincent, and Mervin Keedy, *Elementary Logic for Secondary Schools* (pamphlet). New York: Holt, Rinehart & Winston, Inc., 1962.

Johnson, Donovan, and William Glenn, Series of pamphlets called *Exploring Mathematics on Your Own*. Webster Publishing Co., 1960. See especially *Sets, Sentences, and Operations* and *Topology: The Rubber-Sheet Geometry*.

Just for fun:

Fadiman, Clifton, *Fantasia Mathematica*. New York: Simon and Schuster, Inc., 1958.

Gamow, George, and Marvin Stern, *Puzzle-Math*. New York: The Viking Press, Inc., 1958.

789 2284